# my revisi⏻n notes

# OCR GCSE
# DESIGN and TECHNOLOGY:
## Resistant Materials

**Paul Anderson**

**HODDER**
EDUCATION
AN HACHETTE UK COMPANY

Photo credits: Figure 1.1 © Dena Steiner/iStockphoto.com; Figure 1.2 picsfive – Fotolia; Figure 2.1 drhfoto – Fotolia; Figure 3.1 © travellinglight/iStockphoto.com; Figure 3.2 Xuejun li – Fotolia; Figure 4.1 © Vantage Point – Fotolia.com; Figure 4.2 Andy – Fotolia; Figure 5.1 © Maksym Dragunov/iStockphoto.com; Figure 6.1 © David H. Lewis/iStockphoto.com; Figure 6.2 © MistikaS/iStockphoto.com; Figure 7.1 © Marcus Clackson/iStockphoto.com; Figure 7.2 Flashgaz – Fotolia; Figure 8.1 © Wicki58/iStockphoto.com; Figure 8.2 jörn buchheim – Fotolia; Figure 9.1 © Sebastien Cote/iStockphoto.com; Figure 10.1 Naomi Hasegawa – Fotolia; Figure 14.1 © 2006 Ian Holland/Fotolia.com; Figure 15.3 EYE OF SCIENCE/SCIENCE PHOTO LIBRARY; Figure 17.3 FRANCOISE SAUZE/SCIENCE PHOTO LIBRARY; Figure 19.2 © BAO-RF – Fotolia.com; Figure 25.1 TechSoft UK Ltd; Figure 32.6 C R CLARKE & CO (UK) LIMITED; Figure 37.1 Guillermo lobo – Fotolia; Figure 37.2 © Dan Barnes/iStockphoto.com; Figure 38.1 TechSoft UK Ltd; Figure 38.2 Boxford Limited.

Figures 17.2, 22.1, 24.1, 24.3, 26.1, 29.1, 29.2, 32.5 and 33.3 taken by Stuart Douglas and Ryan Lemon and reproduced with permission.

Every effort has been made to trace and acknowledge the ownership of copyright material. The publishers apologise if inadvertently any sources remain unacknowledged and will be glad to make necessary arrangements at the earliest opportunity.

Orders: please contact Bookpoint Ltd, 130 Milton Park, Abingdon, Oxon OX14 4SB. Telephone: +44 (0)1235 827720. Fax: +44 (0)1235 400454. Lines are open from 9.00a.m. to 5.00p.m., Monday–Saturday, with a 24-hour message-answering service. You can also order through our website: www.hoddereducation.co.uk

If you have any comments to make about this, or any of our other titles, please send them to educationenquiries@hodder.co.uk

*British Library Cataloguing in Publication Data*
A catalogue record for this title is available from the British Library

ISBN: 978 1 4441 68 16 7
This Edition Published 2012
Impression number 10 9 8 7 6 5 4 3 2 1
Year                2017, 2016, 2015, 2014, 2013, 2012

Hachette UK's policy is to use papers that are natural, renewable and recyclable products and made from wood grown in sustainable forests. The logging and manufacturing processes are expected to conform to the environmental regulations of the country of origin.

Cover photo Agb – Fotolia
Typeset by Datapage, India
Printed in Spain for Hodder Education, an Hachette UK Company, 338 Euston Road, London NW1 3BH

# Contents

# Get the most from this book

This book will help you to revise Units A562 Sustainable design and A564 Technical aspects of designing and making.

Use the Revision planner on pages 3 and 4 to plan your revision, topic by topic. Tick each box when you have:

**1** revised and understood a topic

**2** tested yourself

**3** practised the exam questions.

You can also keep track of your revision by ticking off each topic heading in the book. You may find it helpful to add your own notes as you work through each topic.

## Features to help you succeed

Each topic is divided into sections that provide the information that you need to know.

**Tick to track your progress**

### Contents

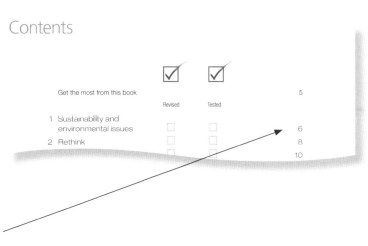

## Examiner tip

Throughout the book there are tips from examiners to help you boost your grade. These identify the typical mistakes candidates make and explain how you can avoid them.

## Glossary

Key words are shown in bold on the pages where they appear. You will find clear, concise definitions of these key words in the Glossary at the end of the book.

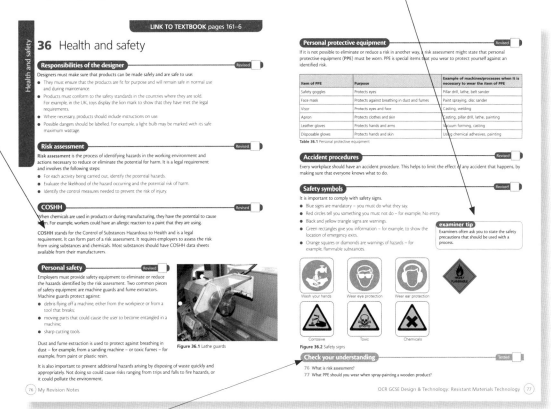

## Check your understanding

These are short, knowledge-based, exam-style questions to provide the first step in testing your learning. They appear at the end of each chapter. Use them to make sure that you have understood every topic. You will find the answers to these questions in a separate section at the end of the book.

Your teacher will be able to provide you with more exam questions from previous examinations. Remember: the more practice questions you do, the better you will do in your examination!

Sustainability and environmental issues

# 1 Sustainability and environmental issues

## Materials selection and the environment
Revised

When selecting the materials to be used in a product, designers have to make sure that they have the properties that the product needs. They also have to consider how the use of those materials will affect the environment when the product is made, during the life of the product and when the product is disposed of at the end of its usable life.

## Sustainability through design
Revised

Making products uses materials and energy. Many of the materials in the products we use on a daily basis, and the sources of energy we use to make these products, are finite resources. This means that as we use them, they are used up and are not replaced. Eventually, these non-sustainable resources will run out.

**Sustainable** resources will not run out. This might be because there is an unlimited supply of the resource, such as sunlight for solar power or wind to power wind turbines; or it might be because the resource is **renewable**. This means that it can be naturally replenished fairly quickly, such as wood from managed forests or plastics made from vegetable products. Using sustainable materials and energy sources means that we could continue to make products with them for as long as we want them – potentially forever.

## Eliminating materials dangerous to the environment
Revised

In the past, some products have used chemicals or materials dangerous to the environment, either as part of the product or during the manufacturing process. For example:

- CFCs are a group of chemicals that were developed in the 1930s. They were an important part of the cooling system in most fridges and freezers. However, in the 1980s it was discovered that they were a main source of harm to the ozone layer.
- Bleach has been used to whiten paper or natural textiles, but it is toxic to fish if it escapes into the water system.
- Lead paint used to be commonly used in houses. It is now known that the dust from the paint is toxic, particularly to small children.

Sometimes, the only way to achieve the specific characteristics needed by a product is to use chemicals and man-made materials that damage the environment. However, the designer must be aware of these chemicals and reduce their use wherever possible.

## Carbon footprint
Revised

**Carbon footprint** is a measure of the greenhouse gases that are produced by a product, a person or a company. These are gases that contribute to global warming, such as carbon dioxide. They may result from:

- the type of materials used, and how much of this material is used, including waste;
- the amount of energy from non-sustainable sources used during manufacture;
- the transportation of goods – if an increased number of products can be fitted on a lorry, each product will have a smaller carbon footprint.

A designer might try to reduce the carbon footprint of a product or to eliminate its effect by carbon offsetting.

**Figure 1.1** Carbon footprint logo

## Carbon offsetting
Revised

**Carbon offsetting** is a method where people and companies invest in projects that reduce their carbon emissions. This includes things like planting trees, recycling or generating energy using solar or wind power. The aim of this is to cancel out the quantity of greenhouse gases that they produce.

## Disposal of products
Revised

Most products do not last forever. Many end up in **landfill** – this is where they are buried under the ground. This can lead to **pollution**.

At the end of their life, products and their packaging need to be disposed of in an environmentally friendly way – this might include reusing the component parts or recycling the materials. Alternatively, products could be designed to be **biodegradable** – that is, they will break down in the ground into natural products.

**Figure 1.2** Burying rubbish on a landfill site

> **examiner tip**
> You need to use key terms like 'sustainability' and 'carbon footprint', and show the examiner that you understand what they mean.

## Check your understanding
Tested

1  What are the meanings of the terms 'sustainable resource' and 'renewable resource'? Give an example of each.
2  Explain how a company could reduce its carbon footprint.

Rethink

# 2 Rethink

## The six Rs

Revised

The six Rs are used by designers as a checklist to reduce the environmental impact of a product. They stand for:

1 Rethink – can what the product does be done in a different way that is less harmful to the environment?
2 Reduce – can the amount of materials (and packaging) in the product be reduced?
3 Reuse – can the parts in the product be used again?
4 Recycle – can the materials used to make the product be reprocessed and used again?
5 Repair – can the life of the product be extended by mending it or carrying out maintenance?
6 Refuse – this means not accepting things that are not the best option for the environment.

Rethink, reduce and refuse are concerned with reducing the amount of resources that are required to make new products. Reuse, recycle and repair reduce the amount of new resources that will be needed to make replacement products.

## Rethink

Revised

Rethink involves looking at the need that a product is addressing and asking if that need can be met in a more environmentally friendly way. This considers not just the choice of materials to make the product, but also its working life and disposal.

## Rethinking design

Revised

This is about approaching design problems differently. Just because previous products have been designed in a certain way, it does not mean that new products have to be designed to be the same.

A designer might look at an existing product and question every feature on it – what is the purpose of this feature? Is it really needed? What properties does this feature need to have? How much material is needed to achieve those properties? How could this be made easier to manufacture? What packaging is needed? By asking questions like these, the designer gains a better understanding of exactly what is required. A product can then be designed to meet this improved understanding of the needs.

Designers might create a product with many functions. This can reduce the total amount of materials needed and also save on energy needs in manufacturing and disposal. For example, who really needs to buy a separate alarm clock, telephone, MP3 player and camera, when all of these functions can now be carried out by a mobile phone?

## Rethinking product life

Designers could consider how the energy used by a product during its life can be reduced. For example, energy-efficient light bulbs have been developed to replace traditional ones. Designers might also consider using alternative sources of energy, such as making a radio that you wind up rather than using batteries.

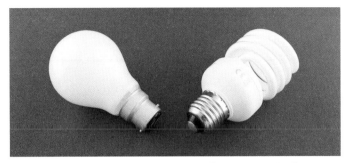

**Figure 2.1** Traditional and energy-efficient light bulbs

## Rethinking disposal

When a product reaches the end of its usable life, it is often thrown away and a replacement is bought. If some parts of the product can be reused, this can help to reduce the need for new resources to make the replacement. This means thinking about how to take the product apart and how to identify the parts or materials that could be reused.

If materials are likely to end up in landfill, designers might think about using biodegradable materials. They might also think about other ways that the product could be disposed of. For example, most packaging ends up as waste. Designers have created packaging materials that contain wild plant seeds – the seeds are part of the packaging. The packaging naturally breaks down quickly and helps the seeds to grow. Some of the products that use this packaging actively encourage littering, as the litter will break down and a patch of wild flowers will grow in its place!

> **examiner tip**
>
> Think about design with an open mind and be aware of the sort of changes that could be made.

## Check your understanding

3 In terms of the six Rs, what is meant by 'rethink'?

4 Films sold on DVD are usually packaged in plastic cases. Give an example of how rethink could be applied to this product.

Reduce

# 3 Reduce

## Reduce
Revised

Reduce means using fewer resources at any stage during the life cycle of a product.

## Product life cycle
Revised

The **product life cycle** is the stages that a new product goes through during its life. These are:

- conception and design;
- making;
- use, including maintenance, if needed;
- disposal.

The designer should consider whether the product's **eco-footprint** can be made smaller at each step of the product life cycle. This is a measure of the impact on the environment. The whole system of looking at a product, from design to disposal, including its use of materials and energy, is referred to as **eco-design**.

One way of reducing the eco-footprint is to reduce waste. In this context, that means anything that does not contribute to the ability of the product to meet the needs it was intended for.

## Reducing material waste during design
Revised

Many products come with some form of packaging. Usually this is thrown away when the product is first used. If this is made from non-renewable materials, such as plastics made from oil, it increases the eco-footprint.

Designers applying reduce might first ask how much packaging is needed. They might also investigate replacing non-renewable materials with sustainable materials, such as card made from wood from managed forests.

**Figure 3.1** Waste packaging awaiting disposal

## Reducing material waste during making
Revised

If material has to be cut or removed to make a product, this often results in scrap and uses energy. The resource requirement can be saved by designing a product so that either:

- it can be made from standard sizes of materials, so less material needs to be cut away; or
- it can be made from **reforming** processes, so there is less waste material.

## Reducing material waste during use
Revised

Many portable electronic products are designed to use batteries. These contain chemicals that can cause pollution if they are disposed of incorrectly to landfill. If these can be replaced by rechargeable batteries, this can reduce the total amount of resources needed during the working life of the product and the amount of chemicals that need to be disposed of.

Similarly, resource needs can be reduced by increasing the efficiency of products. For example, in electronic products the light bulbs used to indicate power on could be replaced with a light-emitting diode, which requires much less electrical power. The efficiency increase means the devices use less power, making the batteries last longer.

**Figure 3.2** Rechargeable battery from a mobile phone

## Reducing material waste during disposal
Revised

Products can be designed so that parts of them can be reused or recycled, reducing the need for new resources to make replacements. They can also be designed from biodegradable materials, which naturally break down in the ground if they are buried as landfill.

## Built-in obsolescence
Revised

Most products have a limited lifetime. **Built-in obsolescence**, also known as planned obsolescence, is where a product has been designed to last for a set period of time. A manufacturer might do this so that they can sell more products: once the product is no longer usable, the user has to buy a replacement.

There are three main types of obsolescence:

● Function – the existing product becomes out of date because new, improved products become available.
● Quality – the product is designed to wear out or break down.
● Desirability – the product is designed to go out of fashion.

Designing products with built-in obsolescence means that additional resources are needed to make the replacement products. When applying reduce, designers might take the opposite approach and consider extending the usable life of a product.

**examiner tip**
When evaluating a product's environmental impact, do not just think about manufacture and the materials used – consider all the stages of the product life cycle.

## Check your understanding
Tested

5 What is meant by 'built-in obsolescence'?
6 State the stages in the product life cycle.

Energy

# 4 Energy

## Energy and manufacturing
Revised

Making products uses energy. Currently, most of the energy we use comes from finite sources, such as coal, oil and gas. Finite means that there is only a certain amount of these resources on our planet. As we use these resources, they are used up and not replaced. Eventually they will run out. Further, using oil, gas and coal produces greenhouse gases, which contribute to global warming and the carbon footprint of the product.

One way to reduce the carbon footprint of a product is to reduce the amount of energy used to make it. If this is not possible, sustainable sources of energy could be used. Sustainable means that they will not run out. Sustainable sources of energy are also carbon neutral – this means that they do not contribute to the carbon footprint of the product they are used to make.

## Making electricity
Revised

The most common type of energy used in manufacturing is electricity. Other sources of energy have to be converted to electricity. In most cases, this involves turning the energy source into rotary motion and using this to turn a turbine. This acts in the opposite way to an electric motor – rather than electricity being used to turn the motor, the turning of the turbine creates electricity.

## Sources of sustainable energy
Revised

### Wind power

Wind can be used to turn propeller-like blades, which turn the turbine. The advantages of wind power are that the wind is free and people who do not live near power lines can use wind turbines to create their own electricity. The disadvantages are that some people think these turbines are not attractive, they can be noisy and they can only produce electricity when there is enough wind to turn the blades.

**Figure 4.1** Solar panels and wind turbines

## Tidal power
Revised

Tidal power converts the energy of water moving in the sea into electricity. The simplest form uses propeller blades located underwater that are moved by currents in the water. It is more expensive to build than a wind turbine, as most of the building has to be done underwater.

## Geothermal energy

Revised

This harnesses the thermal energy stored deep under the earth. Water is pumped down specially drilled holes to great depths, where the heat from the earth turns it to steam. This returns to the surface via other holes, to drive the turbine. Currently, most geothermal plants are located where there is volcanic activity close to the surface. A small geothermal facility can provide sufficient power for a whole village.

## Hydroelectric power

Revised

This involves capturing the energy in moving water. The simplest form is a waterwheel, although this is only able to generate a small amount of electricity. Commercial electric power is generated using dams. These 'trap' large quantities of water, which flow through turbines to produce energy. The advantages of this approach are that once the dam is built there is a constant supply of electricity, and the amount of electricity generated can be controlled by changing the amount of water flowing. However, dams are very expensive to set up and must be built in a suitable location.

Unlike other energy sources, hydroelectric plants can also be used to store energy. If the 'storage' lake supplying the dam is at a higher level than the 'used' water, at times when little electricity is required, the power generated can be used to pump water back up to the storage lake. This can then be allowed to flow back when electricity is needed.

## Solar power

Revised

Solar energy involves harnessing the power of the sun. Unlike other forms of sustainable energy, the electricity is created directly when light falls onto a solar panel. The advantages of solar power are that sunlight is free and electricity can be obtained and used in places where there are no power lines. However, solar panels can be

**Figure 4.2** Hoover Dam – a large hydroelectric dam in the USA

expensive and a large area of land would be needed to capture sufficient amounts to power a town. Also, it only produces electricity when there is sunlight!

## Check your understanding

Tested

7  Explain why using finite resources is not sustainable.

8  Give three examples of sustainable sources of energy.

9  Explain the differences between electricity generation using wind power and solar power.

Refuse

# 5 Refuse

## Refuse
Revised ☐

Refuse means that if something is not the best option for the environment, it should not be accepted. There are several factors that should be considered when evaluating whether a product is the most 'environmentally friendly' option.

## Quantity of materials used
Revised ☐

The amount of material used in a product usually depends on the properties that are required.

A user might refuse to buy a product that contains more material than similar products, as it appears to be wasteful. However, sometimes the 'extra' material is used because the designer has considered additional needs. More material might have been used to reduce the risk of breaking if the product is dropped, providing longer product life. This may be more environmentally friendly, as fewer replacement products would be needed.

## Packaging
Revised ☐

Packaging is useful if it protects a product from being damaged during transportation. However, some products use more packaging than necessary for this, to make the product look more attractive. Some customers have been known to take products out of unnecessary packaging and leave it behind in the shop, rather than accept it!

## Materials we should refuse to use
Revised ☐

Many types of plastic are made from oil. This is not a sustainable resource – it will eventually run out. Unless the properties of the plastic are essential for the product, alternatives should be used. For example, it could be replaced by plastics made from natural sources, such as plants. If the properties of the plastic are not essential, it could be replaced by renewable materials, such as softwood from managed forests.

Metal is made from metal ore, which is a type of rock. Extracting this rock from the ground can cause environmental damage and pollution. This can be limited by using metals that have been recycled. Recycling also reduces energy needs: compared to making steel from metal ore, recycling only uses about 25 per cent of the energy.

**Figure 5.1** A truck being loaded with iron ore in a quarry

Some products use toxic chemicals during production. For example, the colour of paper might be changed to make it 'white' using poisonous chemicals like dioxins. We should consider using products made by more environmentally friendly processes instead.

## Working efficiency
Revised ☐

Working efficiency is the amount of energy or fuel needed to operate the product during its usable life. For example, when deciding which car to buy, some people start by listing the models that meet their needs. They may then choose based on which has the best fuel economy – the one that can travel the furthest distance on a specified amount of fuel.

## Globalisation

Improved transport and communication give large companies more choice over where they manufacture products. Instead of needing factories in every country where a product is sold, they may decide to do all their manufacturing in one 'low-cost' country. The normal reason for doing this is to lower prices to the user or to make more profits.

The products made in this factory will be transported to every market where they are sold. This can be a cause of pollution. Despite the transport cost, the overall cost of making the product may be less, because wages paid to workers may be much lower, and the working hours much longer, than we would be prepared to accept in the UK. The environmental regulations in the country where the factory is may be of a lower standard, leading to increased pollution.

Globalisation means that the user has to make ethical choices – should they benefit from the lower costs or should they refuse to buy the product, due to the working conditions and increased pollution?

## Check your understanding

10 Give an example of a material that we should refuse to use, explaining why it is not the best choice for the environment.

11 Explain the advantages and disadvantages of globalisation.

Reuse

# 6 Reuse

## Reuse

Reuse means using the parts of a product to make other products. The advantage of this is that fewer materials and less energy are needed to make new products.

The item that is reused may be an assembled product or it may be parts that have been removed from products that are no longer required. When planning to reuse the parts in a product, the designer has to consider how the products can be taken apart – this is referred to as **disassembly**.

For more information on disassembly, see Topic 8: Repair on pages 20–21.

When reusing parts it is important to ensure that they have not been damaged or contaminated. This can make them unable or unsuitable to carry out the task. For example, the ink cartridges used in computer printers can be refilled to allow them to be used again. However, if the print head on the cartridge has been damaged, they may leak or not be able to produce printouts of the correct quality.

## Products that can be used again

There are some products where the principle of reusing materials is already well established.

One of the most common types of reused product is rechargeable batteries. These generate far less waste than disposable batteries.

When cars reach the end of their usable life, they are often sent to scrapyards. The parts that are suitable to be used again can be removed and the rest of the car can be sent for recycling or disposal. When a car needs to be repaired, it is usually much cheaper to buy a part from a scrapyard than to buy a new replacement part.

**Figure 6.1** Car bumpers awaiting reuse in a scrapyard

Most supermarkets have bags-for-life available. These reduce the need for disposable plastic bags. Currently, across the world, about 4 trillion disposable plastic bags are used each year. Most end up in landfill or are dumped at sea. It is estimated that 100,000 marine animals are killed each year by disposable plastic bags.

Some local areas around the UK have set up websites and organisations to help people reuse unwanted items. This idea has also been developed on a national level, with organisations such as Freecycle, who match people with things they want to get rid of with people who can use them. Another benefit of using Freecycle is that it promotes community involvement in the process.

In a similar way, there are charities that collect old and unwanted items and redistribute them to other countries where they are needed. For example, old spectacles, mobile phones or shoes are sent to Africa, and old bicycles sent to India.

## Adapting products to alternative uses Revised

Sometimes the reused parts are used to carry out a different task than in the original product. For example, old jam jars or coffee jars can be used to store pencils or nuts and bolts. Old tyres can be used to make swings or as crash protection on the walls of car racing circuits.

In some cases, the part might be cut down to make it suitable for reuse. For example, old tyres can be cut down to make sandals. This is different from recycling, as the materials in the product do not have to be reprocessed.

**Figure 6.2** A race circuit crash barrier made from old tyres

## Check your understanding Tested

12  What is meant by 'reuse'?

13  Give three examples of how products can be reused by adapting them to other uses.

Recycle

# 7 Recycle

## Recycle
Revised

**Recycling** means reprocessing a material so that it can be used to make other products. This usually involves either melting the material or chemically breaking it down into its parts, before making the new product. The advantages of recycling are:

● it reduces the need for new resources;
● the energy requirements to recycle materials are usually much less than the energy requirements to make new materials;
● less material needs to be disposed of in landfill.

If the parts of a product are made from different materials, they must be separated before they can be recycled. In broad terms, there are three types of recycling: primary, secondary and tertiary.

For more information on disassembly, see Topic 8: Repair on pages 20–21.

## Primary recycling
Revised

Primary recycling is using the material to make the same type of product.

For example, an aluminium drinks can could be melted down and made into another drinks can. The energy needed to recycle aluminium is approximately 5 per cent of the energy required to make new metal. According to the US Environmental Protection Agency, in 2009 51 per cent of the aluminium drinks cans used in the USA were made from recycled material.

Similarly, for each tonne of paper that is recycled, approximately 19 trees are saved, along with 26 m³ of water, 320 litres of oil and 2.3 m³ of landfill space.

**Figure 7.1** Paper being recycled at a waste collection plant

## Secondary recycling
Revised

Secondary recycling means reprocessing the material and using it to make a different type of product.

For example, the 'tin cans' used to store food are actually made of steel. These can be recycled to make steel sheets, which are used for car bodywork or the outer panels of washing machines and fridges.

The steel cans can be collected through recycling schemes or extracted from household waste using magnets. The energy needed to recycle steel is about 25 per cent of that needed to make new metal, and recycling makes only 14 per cent of the air pollution. Every tonne of steel that is recycled saves 0.5 tonnes of coal and 1.5 tonnes of iron ore (the rock that is used to make steel).

## Tertiary recycling

Revised

Tertiary recycling involves breaking something down into its raw materials.

PET (polyethylene terephthalate) is commonly used to make plastic bottles. This can be chemically broken down into the basic chemicals used to make several plastics, or even used to make fuel. The high-impact polystyrene used to make vending cups can be broken down and used to make plastic pencils.

**Figure 7.2** A cup and a pencil made from a plastic cup

## Products that use recycled materials

Revised

Recyclable materials include glass, paper, metals, textiles and plastics. Many products made from these materials will include a proportion of recycled material. These products are often marked with symbols so that the materials in them can be visually identified and sorted in recycling schemes.

Most composite materials are not currently recycled, as it is difficult to separate them into the different materials that they are made from.

**Figure 7.3** Recycling symbols

> **examiner tip**
>
> You should be able to explain the different types of recycling.

## Check your understanding

Tested

**14** What is meant by 'secondary recycling'?

**15** Explain why it can be easier to sort steel from domestic waste rather than other types of metal or plastic, even if they are labelled with the correct recycling symbols.

**Repair**

# 8 Repair

## Repair

Revised

Repair is often used to refer to mending or replacing broken products. However, it means any activity that extends the life of a product. This includes:

- replacing worn-out parts;
- changing the batteries in electrical products;
- repainting a product to stop it rusting;
- maintenance, to stop parts wearing out or breaking.

Repairing products means that less material and energy is needed to make replacements.

Some manufacturers see repair as a bad thing, as it reduces their sales. This is because they make money by selling products, and the longer their products last, the longer there is between sales, so they make less money. However, they can still make profits while designing to allow repair, as they can sell the parts that need to be replaced in their products.

**Figure 8.1** Example of a repair activity – replacing the worn-out sole on a shoe

**Figure 8.2** Servicing a car to extend the engine life

## Disassembly

Revised

Disassembly means taking a product apart. This is important for repair, as parts may need to be replaced. It is also very important for reuse and recycling, where parts and materials will need to be removed and identified.

The designer must consider how parts can be taken out of the product. This may affect the design of the product and the fabrication and joining processes used to make it. For example:

- the product might include an access panel or door, so that any mechanisms inside it are easy to get to;
- the product might be designed as a series of modules, so that if something goes wrong, a module can be replaced quickly and easily; although this uses more resources than just replacing a part, it has the advantage that the repair can usually be carried out by someone with less skill;
- the product could be held together using a temporary joining technique, such as screws, so that it is easy to take apart;
- the use of permanent joining methods, such as adhesives, nails, rivets or welding, would be avoided.

Sometimes a manufacturer will deliberately make it difficult to take products apart. For example, many mobile phones use non-standard screws that require special tools. This is to prevent untrained people from interfering with the inside of the product, which might cause damage and limit its life. The phone can still be repaired by specialists who have the tools.

For more information on joining processes, see Topics 20, 21 and 35: Pre-manufactured components, Fixtures and fittings, and Fabricating on pages 44–7 and 74–5.

## Products that cannot be repaired Revised

Many low-cost items that are produced in large quantities are not designed for repair. This is because it would cost more to fix the product than to replace it. For example, in cheap digital watches the electronic circuit is usually very small. If the circuit went wrong, expensive specialist equipment would be needed to examine it, plus a store of the miniaturised components and special equipment to repair it. This could require a lot of labour time, which would usually be far more than the cost of the parts.

Some products cannot be repaired as it may be dangerous to do so. For example:

- electrical circuits may be dangerous if they contain electrical charge in capacitors;
- the cooling system in an old fridge contains chemicals that are very hazardous to the environment;
- a broken electrical plug may not be as strong if it is repaired, leading to an increased risk that it will break again and cause injury.

## Check your understanding Tested

16 List two design features that show that a product has been designed for disassembly.

17 Name two products that cannot be repaired and explain why this is the case.

# 9 Product design

## Design and our quality of life

Revised ☐

Products are designed to meet needs. The needs might be problems or they might be opportunities for improvement. Either way, good design can improve our quality of life. Without design, we would have no cars to transport us, no fridges to store our food, no televisions to watch, and no MP3 players to listen to.

An important feature of good design is that it meets the needs of the user. These can include how the product works, what it looks like, what it is made from, how much it costs and what size it is.

## Anthropometrics and ergonomics

Revised ☐

**Anthropometrics** is the study of body sizes and properties. **Ergonomics** is using these data to ensure that a product is the right fit for its user. For example, a spoon designed for a small child will be smaller than one designed for an adult. This is because the hand and mouth of the child are much smaller than those of an adult. Ergonomically designed products are usually more comfortable for the user.

## Design evolution

Revised ☐

Product designs are constantly changing and evolving, for a variety of reasons.

### Changing styles and tastes

Needs change over time. The design of products often changes in response to the changing needs of the users. This is known as 'market pull'.

One reason for changing needs is fashion. Styles and tastes can change quickly – for example, to copy famous people or celebrities.

### Developments in technology

These include the development of new or improved materials and manufacturing processes. Sometimes these developments allow new products to be designed. These may be able to meet needs that previously could not be met.

For example, telephones met a need to be able to communicate with people who were some distance away. Originally, they all had to be attached to a phone line. Developments in radio technology allowed the development of mobile phones, so that people could also keep in touch with each other while out and about. The first commercial mobile phone was launched in Japan in 1978. These early phones were bigger and heavier than house bricks. Further developments that have allowed them to become the products we know today include:

● improvements in battery technology – they are now smaller, but can produce more electricity;

● reductions in the size of electronic components;

● developments in manufacturing technology, to allow the increasingly small components to be assembled by computer-controlled machines.

Alternatively, some innovative products can create needs that users were not previously aware of. For example, how many people knew that they needed a mobile phone that could take pictures or access the internet before these products were available?

**Figure 9.1** An old house phone and a smartphone

## Environmental pressures                                                        Revised ☐

Our understanding of how the products we use affect our environment is continually developing. Designers and users are becoming more aware of environmental pressures in product design, due to issues such as increases in the cost of non-renewable resources, pollution and global warming.

Environmental pressures have led to some designers adopting an approach called eco-design. This involves considering the whole life of a product when it is being designed, from design to disposal, including its use of materials and energy.

For more information on eco-design, see Topic 3: Reduce on pages 10–11.

## Globalisation                                                                   Revised ☐

Developments in transport and communication have led to increased **globalisation** of products. A product might be designed in one country, manufactured in another, and then sold all over the world. This means that designers have to take into account the different needs of several different markets when developing a new product.

For more information on globalisation, see Topic 5: Refuse on pages 14–15.

## Check your understanding                                                        Tested ☐

18 Give an example of an ergonomically designed product and explain which features are ergonomic.

19 State three possible reasons why product designs change, giving an example of each.

# 10 Social, moral and cultural issues

*Social, moral and cultural issues*

## Social issues and design — Revised

Designing and making products have a big effect on our society and how it is developing.

A designer must consider how designs affect people other than the user of the product. For example, the development of personal MP3 players gives individuals more choice about what music they can listen to when travelling on public transport. However, some other passengers can get very annoyed at the noise from the headphones, so the designer may consider ways in which this can be reduced.

## Inclusive design — Revised

People are all different. If a designer creates products suitable for the average user, then a large number of people may not be able to use them. For example:

- people with visual impairments will not be able to read the signs and symbols on a product;
- wheelchair users may not be able to reach high shelves or switches;
- people with hearing impairments may not be able to hear alarms or warning bells.

Society has expectations that products should be designed so that they can be used by people with physical disabilities. This is known as **inclusive design**.

## Moral issues — Revised

Moral judgements are decisions about what is considered acceptable and not acceptable in society. This can be complicated, as the views of society change over time.

## Conditions of working — Revised

Our society wants products to be available at a low cost. We also want workers to have a safe working environment. Other countries may have different standards of what is acceptable – for example, they may allow children to be employed for long hours at very low wages.

With increased globalisation, manufacturers have more choice over where they can make products. They have to make a moral judgement between cost and the working conditions of the people who make the products.

Some companies, non-governmental organisations and trade union organisations have formed an alliance called the Ethical Trading Initiative (ETI). Its aim is to ensure that a suitable standard of working conditions is achieved for all workers.

## Protecting users — Revised

Designers and manufacturers sometimes have to make moral decisions between the cost of a product and how safe it is. For example, they may decide to use a cheaper but less strong material, knowing that there is an increased risk of it failing over time.

Culture is the way that history, beliefs and tradition have influenced a group of people. Usually this group shares a common interest or has similar values. This might be because they all live in the same country, all share the same religious beliefs or all like the same type of music.

Culture has a big influence on the products that the people in that group use and the things that they value. For example:

● In the UK, we traditionally eat dinner sitting at a table. In Japan, the tradition is to eat dinner while sitting on the floor. As a result, Japanese dining tables have very short legs!

● In South Africa, red is the colour of mourning. In China, red symbolises good fortune. The responses of these two societies to the same red product may be very different.

● In the Middle East and Africa, products might be considered more attractive if they have traditional patterns or designs on them. In Europe, the influence of industrial design can mean that greater value may be awarded to a simple design without a pattern.

● Animals can be seen in different ways by different cultures. In Europe, piggy banks are often given to children to encourage them to save money. However, in some Middle Eastern countries, pigs are regarded as unclean, and presenting an image of a pig to a person could be an insult.

Some products can be sold in many countries, each with different cultural values. Designers must be aware of the feelings of others and consider how the cultures of all these different potential users may influence the product.

**Figure 10.1** Traditional Japanese table

20 What is meant by inclusive design?

21 What is the aim of the Ethical Trading Initiative?

# 11 Properties of materials

## Classifications of materials

Materials are usually divided into different types, depending on what they were made from or their properties. The commonly used types are:

- wood and manufactured board;
- metals;
- thermoplastics and thermosets;
- composite materials;
- smart and modern materials.

Within a type, there can be a big variation between the properties of different materials.

## Properties of resistant materials

Different materials have different properties. Designers have to select materials with the properties that are needed by the product.

### Strength

The **strength** of a material is its ability to resist breaking when a force is applied to it. If the force is trying to stretch the material, this is resisted by the tensile strength. If the force is trying to squash the material, this is resisted by the compressive strength.

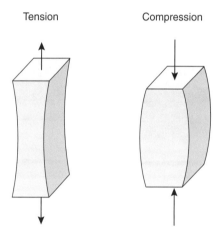

Tension          Compression

**Figure 11.1** Types of strength

### Hardness

**Hardness** is the ability of a material to resist cutting, scratches and indentations to its surface.

### Impact resistance

Impact resistance is the ability of a material to withstand a knock or a blow without breaking.

### Toughness

**Toughness** is the extent to which a material can withstand lots of knocks and blows without breaking. It is the opposite of being brittle.

## Elasticity

**Elasticity** shows how much a material can be stretched or deformed and still return to its original shape.

## Ductility

**Ductility** is a measure of how much a material can be stretched without breaking.

## Flexibility

**Flexibility** is how easy the material is to bend without permanently changing shape. If a material is not flexible, it is said to be rigid or stiff.

## Malleability

The **malleability** of a material is how easy it is to permanently change its shape without breaking. It shows how easy it is to hammer, roll or press a material into a different shape.

## Chemical resistance

The **chemical resistance** of a material is its ability to resist being damaged by chemicals.

## Thermal and electrical conductivity

**Thermal** and **electrical conductivity** indicate how easily heat and electricity pass through a material.

## Strength-to-weight ratio

**Strength-to-weight ratio** is a measure of the strength of the material compared to its weight. This is important for products such as aeroplane wings, where the amount of material used will be based on the strength needed by the product.

## Aesthetic qualities
Revised

Aesthetic means how well an object appeals to the five senses. This includes:

- what the product looks like – its colour, shape, whether it is shiny or dull;
- whether the surface is rough or smooth to touch – for example, the handle of a tennis racket may be rough, to make it easier to grip;
- what the material tastes and smells like – this is important if you are making a bowl to hold food or a toy that a small child might put in its mouth;
- what sound is made by the product – this could be how loud the siren of an alarm is or the musical note made when a bell is struck.

Which aesthetic qualities are important for a product will depend on what the product is designed to do.

> **examiner tip**
>
> When explaining why a material is suitable for a product, or when comparing materials, you get marks for using the names of the properties.

## Check your understanding
Tested

22 Which properties would be the most important for each of the following products?
- A bicycle tyre
- The wing of an airliner
- A disposable cup from a drinks machine
- The body of an electric kettle

23 A manufacturer is pressing a bar of metal through a small hole to make it into a wire. Which properties of the metal would be important in this application, and why?

Wood and manufactured board

# 12 Wood and manufactured board

## Woods

There are two main types of wood:

● **hardwood** comes from deciduous trees, which lose their leaves in the autumn;

● **softwood** comes from coniferous trees, which remain evergreen all year round.

These names do not mean that hardwoods are hard or that softwoods are soft. Softwoods usually grow faster than hardwoods, so are generally cheaper.

| Name | Properties/working characteristics | Uses |
|---|---|---|
| Beech | Very tough, hard, straight and close-grained; it withstands wear and shocks; polishes well; liable to warp | Chairs, flooring, tools, turned items, toys, steam-bent furniture |
| Oak | Heavy, hard, tough, open-grain, finishes well; good outdoors; corrodes steel screws, leaving a blue stain | Boatbuilding, floors, gateposts, high-class furniture and fittings |
| Mahogany | Polishes quite well, but has interlocking grain, which makes it difficult to work | Indoor furniture, shop fittings, veneers used to face manufactured boards |

**Table 12.1** Common hardwoods

| Name | Properties/working characteristics | Uses |
|---|---|---|
| Redwood (Scots pine) | Straight grain, knotty, easy to work, finishes well, durable; widely available and relatively cheap | Commonly used for construction work; needs protection when used outdoors |
| Western red cedar | Lightweight, knot-free, straight grain, contains natural oils that protect it from weather; fine silky surface | Outdoor joinery, e.g. cladding of buildings, wall panelling |
| Parana pine | Hard, straight grain, almost knot-free, available in wide boards | Good-quality inside joinery, such as staircases and built-in furniture |

**Table 12.2** Common softwoods

### The forms in which wood can be bought

Wood first has to be cut from the tree. This is known as conversion. Usually, it is then dried. This is known as **seasoning**. Finally, it is machined into the **form** it will be sold in.

Usually, it is sawn into a standard size and shape. Rough-sawn timber is often planed to give it a smooth surface. Planing makes the wood approximately 3 mm smaller on each face than the sawn size. Planed timber is more expensive than sawn timber. However, it has a smoother finish and accurate size.

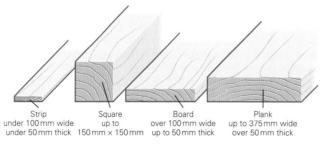

Strip
under 100 mm wide
under 50 mm thick

Square
up to
150 mm × 150 mm

Board
over 100 mm wide
up to 50 mm thick

Plank
up to 375 mm wide
over 50 mm thick

**Figure 12.1** Standard timber sections

Some timber is made into different shapes, called **mouldings**. This is done by machining it using special cutters. Mouldings are often used for decorative purposes, such as skirting boards or the trim around other wooden parts.

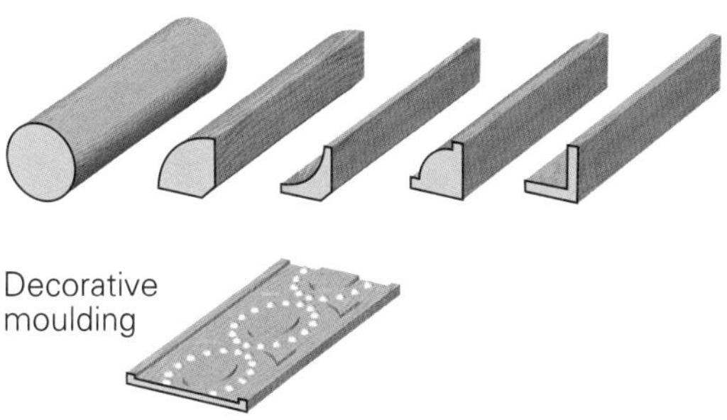

## Manufactured board Revised

**Manufactured boards** are wood-based materials. They are usually less expensive than solid timber and can be much larger sizes. Sheets as large as 2440 × 1220 mm are readily available. Their properties are not affected by the grain of the wood and they are stable products – they will not twist and warp like green timber.

### MDF

MDF (medium-density fibreboard) is made by compressing and gluing tiny wood particles and fibres together. It has no grain and a smooth surface. It is often used to make indoor furniture.

### Plywood

Plywood is made by gluing together thin strips of wood, called veneers. Each strip is glued with the grain running at 90 degrees to the previous one. For uses such as furniture panels, the appearance can be improved by using top and bottom veneers made from high-quality hardwood.

### Blockboard

Blockboard is made by gluing softwood strips side by side. These are sandwiched between thin strips of wood, known as plies. The grain of the plies runs at 90 degrees to the softwood strips. It is used in furniture, such as tabletops.

### Chipboard

Chipboard is made by compressing small chips of wood together with glue. It is very inexpensive, but can be difficult to work with, as the surface is quite rough. For applications such as kitchen worktops, it is usually covered with a veneer or a thin layer of plastic to improve its appearance.

### Hardboard

Hardboard is made by squeezing small wood fibres together with glue. Usually, one side of the board is smooth and the other has a rough texture. It has lower strength than other manufactured boards. It is often used in applications where it is out of sight, such as drawer bottoms or the backs of cupboards.

Standard sections

Decorative moulding

**Figure 12.2** Timber mouldings

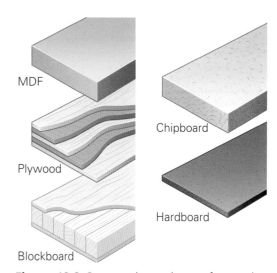

MDF

Chipboard

Plywood

Hardboard

Blockboard

**Figure 12.3** Commonly used manufactured boards

## Check your understanding Tested

24 What does 'MDF' stand for?

25 A furniture company is considering making a dining table. They are considering making it from a hardwood, a softwood or a manufactured board.

   a Give one example of each of these materials that would be suitable for this application.

   b Recommend which material should be used and explain your choice.

Metals

# 13 Metals

## Metals

Revised

Metal is mined from the ground as metal ore. This is processed to extract the metal and then refined to remove impurities. These activities can disfigure the landscape, cause pollution and use lots of energy. This is one of the reasons why metals are recycled or reused. All metals can be recycled.

**Pure metals** are made from a single element, such as aluminium or copper. However, most metals are mixed with other metals or elements to improve their properties. The name for a mixture of two or more metals is an **alloy**.

There are two 'families' of metals:

- **Ferrous metals** contain iron. Usually they also contain carbon, with the amount depending on the properties needed from the metal.
- **Non-ferrous metals** do not contain iron.

| Metal | Composition | Properties/working characteristics | Uses |
|---|---|---|---|
| Cast iron | Re-melted pig iron with additions | Hard skin, but brittle soft core; rigid under compression, but cannot be bent or forged | Heavy crushing machines, car cylinder blocks, machine parts, vices |
| Mild steel | Alloy of iron and 0.15–0.30% carbon | High tensile strength, ductile, tough, fairly malleable, poor resistance to corrosion | General purpose, nails, screws, nuts and bolts, plate, sheet, tube, girders, car bodies |
| Medium-carbon steel | 0.30–0.70% carbon | Stronger and harder than mild steel, but less ductile, tough and malleable | Garden tools, such as trowels and forks, springs |
| High-carbon steel | 0.70–1.40% carbon | Hardest of the carbon steels; less ductile, tough or malleable | Hammers, chisels, screwdrivers, drills, files, taps and dies |
| Stainless steel | Alloy of steel with 18% chrome and 8% nickel | Resistant to corrosion, hard, tough; difficult to work | Sinks, dishes, cutlery |

**Table 13.1** Common ferrous metals

| Metal | Composition | Properties/working characteristics | Uses |
|---|---|---|---|
| Aluminium | Pure metal | Light, soft, ductile, malleable, good conductor of heat and electricity, corrosion-resistant, polishes well | Aircraft bodies, saucepans, cooking utensils, packaging, foils, cans, window frames |
| Duralumin | 4% copper, 1% manganese and magnesium | Equivalent strength as mild steel, but much lighter, ductile, machines well, work hardens | Aircraft and vehicle parts |
| Copper | Pure metal | Malleable, ductile, tough, good conductor of heat/electricity, easily joined, corrosion-resistant | Electrical wire, hot-water tanks, central-heating pipes, printed circuit boards |
| Brass | Alloy of 65% copper, 35% zinc | Corrosion-resistant; heat and electrical conductor, easily joined; casts well | Castings, forgings, ornaments, boat fittings |

Continued...

| Metal | Composition | Properties/working characteristics | Uses |
|---|---|---|---|
| Bronze | Alloy of 90% copper, 10% tin | Tough, hard-wearing, corrosion-resistant | Bearings, castings for statues, coins; air, water and steam valves |
| Lead | Pure metal | Very soft, heaviest common metal, malleable, corrosion-resistant, low melting point, easy to work | Soft solders, roof coverings, protection against X-ray radiation |
| Zinc | Pure metal | Poor strength-to-weight ratio, low melting point, extremely corrosion-resistant, easily worked | Coating (galvanising) steel, e.g. traditional watering cans, buckets and dustbins, intricate die-castings |

**Table 13.2** Common non-ferrous metals

## The forms in which metal can be bought
Revised

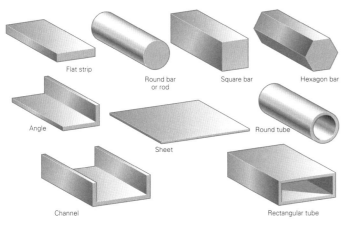

Flat strip

Round bar or rod

Square bar

Hexagon bar

Angle

Sheet

Round tube

Channel

Rectangular tube

**Figure 13.1** Standard metal forms

**examiner tip**

When writing about a material, use its name rather than its 'type'. For example, say mild steel or aluminium, rather than metal.

Most common metals are available in a wide range of standard shapes and sizes. However, as different shapes are used for different purposes, not all metals are made in the full range of standard forms. Designers try to use these standard forms to save time and energy when machining metal products.

## Check your understanding
Tested

26 What is a non-ferrous metal?
27 Explain why steel is an alloy.
28 Name two ferrous metals, two pure non-ferrous metals and two non-ferrous metal alloys.
29 Which metal would be a good choice for cooking pans that are used to heat food on gas cookers? Explain your choice.

# 14 Thermoplastics and thermosets

## Thermoplastics and thermosets — Revised

Most plastics are made from crude oil, by a complex series of chemical reactions. Oil is a non-renewable resource.

Some modern plastics are made from sustainable sources, such as plants. These plastics are often biodegradable. This means that they will rot away if they are thrown away as landfill.

**Figure 14.1** Drilling for oil

There are two main types of plastic:

● **Thermoplastics** will soften when heated, allowing their shape to be changed; they will harden into the new shape as they cool. This process can be repeated many times.
● Thermosetting plastics, also known as **thermosets** – once formed into a shape, their shape cannot be changed by heating them again.

When making plastic, the properties of the material can be changed by adding extra substances to them:

● Plasticisers are added to make the plastic soft and pliable.
● Pigments are added to colour the plastic.
● Fillers are added to increase the 'bulk' of the material, reducing the amount of chemicals that is needed to make a product.

A common advantage of many plastics is that they can easily be formed directly into the shape of the product. This means that compared to other materials, the costs to make a product can often be lower.

## Thermoplastics — Revised

Thermoplastics are the most widely used type of plastics. They can usually be recycled.

Thermoplastics are available as sheet material of standard sizes. These can be heated and re-formed to make a wide range of products. They can also be bought in powder form, so they can be melted to be made into the desired shape.

| Name | Properties/working characteristics | Uses |
|---|---|---|
| Low-density polythene | Range of colours, tough, flexible, good electrical insulator and chemical resistance | Detergent and squeezy bottles, bin liners, carrier bags |
| High-density polythene | Range of colours, hard, stiff, good chemical resistance, high impact | Milk crates, bottles, pipes, buckets, bowls |
| PVCu | Stiff, hard, tough, good chemical and weather resistance | Pipes, guttering, roofing sheets, window frames |
| Polystyrene | Range of colours, stiff, hard, lightweight, safe with food, good water resistance | Disposable plates, cups, model kits, food containers |
| Polypropylene | Hard and lightweight, good chemical and impact resistance, can be sterilised, easily welded together, resistance to work fatigue | Medical equipment, syringes, crates, string, rope, chair shells, containers with integral (built-in) hinges, kitchenware |
| Nylon | Hard, tough, resilient to wear, self-lubricating, resistant to chemicals and high temperatures | Gear wheels, bearings, curtain-rail fittings, clothing, combs, hinges |
| Acrylic | Stiff, hard, clear, durable outdoors, easily machined and polished, good range of colours, excellent impact resistance (glass substitute); does scratch easily | Illuminated signs, aircraft canopies, car rear-light clusters, baths, Perspex™ sheet |

Table 14.1 Common thermoplastics

## Thermosets
Revised

Thermosets are particularly useful for making products that need to keep their shape and are resistant to heat. They are usually available as different chemicals, which must be mixed together to make the thermoset directly into the shape it is needed to be. They cannot usually be recycled.

| Name | Properties/working characteristics | Uses |
|---|---|---|
| Urea-formaldehyde | Stiff, hard, brittle, heat-resistant, good electrical insulator, range of colours | White electrical fittings, domestic appliance parts, wood glue |
| Melamine-formaldehyde | Stiff, hard, strong, range of colours, scratch- and stain-resistant, odourless | Tableware, decorative laminates for work surfaces, electrical insulation |
| Phenol-formaldehyde | Stiff, hard, strong, brittle, heat-resistant | Dark electrical fittings, saucepan and kettle handles |
| Epoxy resin | Good chemical and wear resistance, resists heat to 250°C, electrical insulator | Adhesive such as Araldite™ used to bond different materials such as wood, metal and porcelain |
| Polyester resin | When laminated with glass fibre becomes tough, hard and strong; brittle without reinforcement | GRP boats, chair shells, car bodies |

Table 14.2 Common thermosetting plastics

> **examiner tip**
>
> Make sure you understand the difference between a thermoplastic and a thermosetting plastic and can name examples of both types.

## Check your understanding
Tested

30 What is the difference between a thermoplastic and a thermosetting plastic?

31 A company is designing a plastic bowl that will be used to heat food in a microwave oven. What type of plastic would you recommend that they use? Explain your answer.

# 15 Changing material properties

## Heat treatment of metals ⟨Revised⟩

The properties of some metals can be changed by heating and cooling the metal in a controlled way.

### Hardening and tempering

This process is used to harden high-carbon steels, which contain 0.8–1.4 per cent carbon.

Ferrous metals can be hardened using a process called **quenching**. This involves heating the steel above its lower critical point, then plunging it into oil or water. This cools it very quickly, making it harder, but brittle.

**Tempering** involves heating the steel to between 230°C and 300°C, then quenching it again. This increases its toughness.

### Case hardening

**Case hardening** is used to harden mild steels containing less than 0.4 per cent carbon. It changes the surface of the mild steel into a hard skin of high-carbon steel. First, the steel is heated and either put in a special gas atmosphere or dipped in carbon powder. This is called **carburising** and makes the surface absorb carbon. The surface is then hardened by quenching. As the hard skin is very thin, no tempering is needed.

### Normalising

Many metals get harder when they are bent or hammered. This is known as **work hardening**.

**Normalising** is used for work-hardened steel. It makes it tougher and more ductile. It involves heating the steel above its upper critical point, then allowing it to cool in still air.

### Annealing

**Annealing** is used for both ferrous and non-ferrous metals. It makes work-hardened metal softer and easier to work. It involves heating the metal and allowing it to cool slowly.

## Composite materials ⟨Revised⟩

**Composite materials** are made by combining two or more different materials to produce better properties.

Unlike an alloy, the materials in the composite are not bonded together chemically. If you take a section through a composite material, you can still make out the different materials that it is made from. As it is difficult to separate the materials, they cannot usually be recycled.

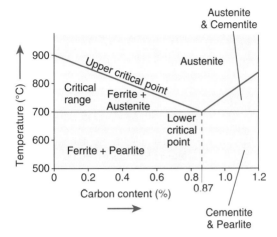

**Figure 15.1** Structure of steel at different temperatures

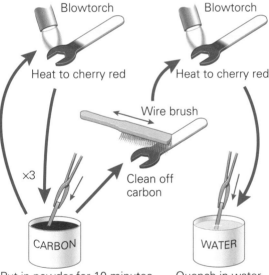

Put in powder for 10 minutes    Quench in water

**Figure 15.2** Case hardening of a mild steel spanner

Some of the most common composites are made using strands of fibre in a matrix of resin. These are made by placing the fibres in a mould and coating them with liquid resin, which hardens to form the composite.

## Glass-reinforced plastic

Glass-reinforced plastic (GRP) is known as fibreglass. It is made from glass fibres in a matrix of polyester resin. It is light and can be moulded, but is stronger than plastic. It is used to make canoes and the hulls of boats.

## Carbon-fibre reinforced plastic

Carbon-fibre reinforced plastic (CRP) combines the strength of carbon fibre with the rigidity of polyester resin. It is stronger and tougher than GRP, but more expensive. It is used to make the body shells of high-performance sports cars and the frames of racing bikes.

## Kevlar

Kevlar™ is a type of polymer that is made as fibres. It is flexible, very difficult to cut or break and, weight for weight, it is up to five times stronger than steel. Ceramic plates are very hard and rigid, but brittle. By combining layers of Kevlar™ with ceramic plates, it is possible to make lightweight, bullet-proof armour.

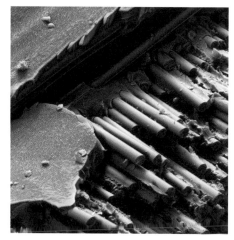

**Figure 15.3** Section through a piece of fibreglass, magnification ×600; the glass fibres are surrounded by a plastic matrix

## Check your understanding

Tested

32 Explain the differences between hardening and annealing.

33 Describe the heat treatment process used to increase the toughness of work-hardened mild steel.

34 What is meant by the term 'composite material'?

35 Give two examples of the use of composite materials.

LINK TO TEXTBOOK pages 55–60

# 16 Finishing processes

## Reasons for using finishing processes
Revised

**Finishing** involves changing the surface of a product to improve its properties. It might be used to improve corrosion resistance, provide greater protection from wear, or to improve the appearance of a product. The type of finishing used will depend on the type of material and the reason it is needed.

## Finishes for metal
Revised

The surface of a metal product must be cleaned to remove any oil or grease before a finishing process is used. If a bright finish is required for steel, it might be draw filed along its length and cleaned with emery cloth. Copper and brass may be pickled in acid to remove metal oxides.

### Paint

**Painting** is often the cheapest and easiest way of adding colour to metal and improving its corrosion resistance. When painting bare metal, a primer, such as red oxide or zinc chromate, is applied first. This helps the other coats to adhere to the metal.

Acrylic and cellulose paints can be applied by brush or spray. They give a hard and durable finish. Cellulose-based paint can be applied without the need for a primer.

### Dip-coating

This coats the metal with a layer of plastic. It adds colour and gives excellent protection. Refrigerator shelves are dip-coated.

The metal part is heated to 180–200°C. It is then dipped into a fluidised bath of polyethylene powder for a few seconds. 'Fluidised' means that air is blown through the powder to make it behave like a liquid. The polyethylene sticks to the hot metal and it is left to cool.

### Galvanising

Galvanising involves dipping a steel product into a bath of molten zinc. The zinc forms a protective coating, which improves the corrosion resistance of the steel.

### Electroplating

**Electroplating** uses a process called electrolysis to coat a metal with a thin layer of another metal. The part to be coated is put in a tank containing a chemical solution and an electrical contact. An electrical current is passed through the part and a thin layer of metal slowly builds up on it.

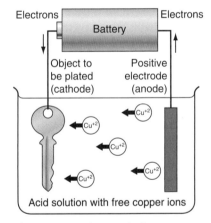

**Figure 16.1** Electroplating

| Coating metal | Property improved | Typical application |
|---|---|---|
| Zinc | Corrosion resistance | Car body panels (under the paint) |
| Nickel | Corrosion resistance, bright appearance | Bicycle and motorcycle frames |
| Tin | Non-toxic, corrosion resistance | Food cans |
| Chromium | Shiny appearance | Taps, car bodywork |

**Table 16.1** Common electroplated coatings

Parts that are chrome-plated are usually nickel-plated first to improve their corrosion resistance.

Wood is usually planed and sanded before finishing. When varnish or paint is used, if more than one coat is applied, the wood is usually rubbed down between each coat.

| Finish | Method of application | Properties of the finish |
|---|---|---|
| Oil | Rub into the surface with a cloth | Adds shine and makes the grain stand out; provides some protection against moisture |
| Wax | Rub into the surface with a cloth; buff after it has dried | Adds shine; provides some protection against moisture |
| French polish | Rubbed in using cotton wool wrapped in a cloth | Adds shine, provides some protection against moisture |
| Stain | Cloth or brush | Changes the colour of the wood |
| Sealer | Brush, rub down with glasspaper when dry | Adds shine; provides good protection against moisture |
| Polyurethane varnish | Brush or spray | Adds shine; provides very good protection against moisture |
| Yacht varnish | Brush or spray | Adds shine, waterproof |
| Paint | Brush or spray | Changes the colour, hides the natural appearance of the wood; provides good protection against moisture |

**Table 16.2** Finishes for wood

## Finishes for plastic       Revised

Finishing processes are not usually used with plastics. The processes used to make plastic products, such as injection moulding, give them a very high-quality surface finish – this is known as 'self-finishing'. Plastics are coloured during their manufacturing process. If there are small scratches and marks on the product, these can be removed by **polishing** with a buffing machine.

## Check your understanding       Tested

36 Describe the process of electroplating a metal item.

37 A manufacturer is making high-quality garden furniture from hardwood. Which finish would you recommend to protect it against rain? Explain your choice.

# 17 Smart materials

## Smart materials
Revised

A **smart material** has a property that reacts to changes in its environment. This change is reversible when the environment changes again. It can also be repeated many times.

The change in the environment could be light or pressure or temperature. The property that is changed depends on the material. It might be the shape, the colour, the electrical conductivity, and so on.

## Shape memory alloy
Revised

When a 'normal' metal is bent beyond its elastic limit, its shape is changed permanently. However, for a shape memory alloy (SMA) such as nitonol, if it is then heated to a certain temperature it will return to its original shape. This temperature is known as the transition temperature. It could be reached by putting the SMA in hot water or, for wire made from SMA, by passing an electrical current through it.

SMA is used in three types of application:

● to respond to changes in temperature – for example, the triggers for fire alarm systems;
● where movement is needed from an electrical signal – for example, electric door locks and artificial muscles in robot arms;
● to allow the quick repair of 'damaged' products – for example, spectacle frames, which are sometimes bent accidentally by the user.

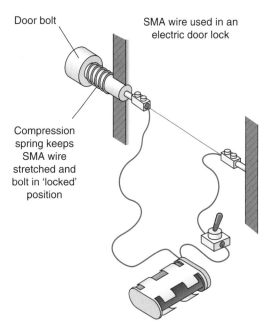

**Figure 17.1** Electric door lock using SMA wire: when a current is applied, the wire coils up, releasing the bolt

## Thermochromic materials

**Thermochromic** materials change colour at specific temperatures. They are available as sheets of plastic or as pigments. The pigments can be used to colour other materials or paints. They can be used to make plastic strip thermometers or food packaging that changes colour when the product is cooked to the right temperature.

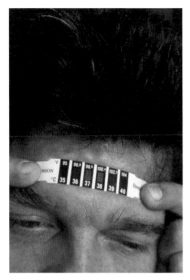

**Figure 17.2** Using a thermometer made from thermochromic strip

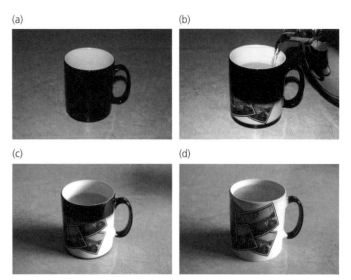

**Figure 17.3** Colour change on a mug coated with ink containing a thermochromic pigment

## Photochromic materials

**Photochromic** materials change colour in response to changes in the level of light. They are used for applications such as the lenses of sunglasses that become lighter or darker, or security markers that can be seen only in ultraviolet light.

## Smart grease

When you press into smart grease slowly, it moves like normal grease. However, when you try to push into it fast, it becomes hard. It is used to 'damp' or soften the movement of drawers on DVD players.

## Check your understanding

38 What is meant by a 'smart material'?

39 List three smart materials. For each, give an example of an application where it could be used.

# 18 Modern materials and nanotechnology

## Modern materials
Revised

The process of developing new materials never stops. This section outlines some of the more recent developments.

### Flexiply

Flexiply is a type of bendable plywood that can easily be bent to shape by hand, without special equipment. It can be used to make curved furniture or shop counters.

### Flexi-veneer

'Traditional' wood veneer can be quite brittle; it cracks or splits when bent. Flexi-veneer can be bent in any direction without splitting. It is a paper-backed product, 0.8 mm thick, supplied on a roll. It can be used to give a decorative finish on furniture made from low-cost materials.

### Hexaboard

Hexaboard is a plywood with a layer of PVC plastic on both faces. The plastic has a characteristic hexagonal pattern, which gives the board its name. It is light, strong, very durable and has good impact resistance. It is used to make protective cases for instruments.

### Anodised aluminium sheet

This is aluminium sheet that has been treated in a chemical tank with an electric current. It has a harder surface than untreated aluminium and can absorb permanent dye. It is used to make coloured products, including jewellery, aircraft parts and window frames.

### Aluminium composite sheet

Aluminium composite sheet is made from a sheet of polythene sandwiched between two sheets of aluminium. The aluminium can be painted or given different finishes, depending on the appearance that is needed. It is rigid, lightweight and weather-resistant. It is used to make road signs or to cover the outside of buildings.

## Nanotechnology
Revised

Nanotechnology is concerned with controlling matter on an atomic scale, to form it into systems or materials with different properties. Carbon provides a good example of how changing the structure of matter at this scale can change its properties:

- If the carbon atoms are arranged randomly, it produces soot.

- In one arrangement, it is graphite. Graphite is a 'soft' form of carbon used in pencils.

- Arranged another way, it is diamond. This is incredibly hard.

- Arranged in yet another way, it can form carbon nanotubes. These have the potential to be hundreds of times stronger than steel.

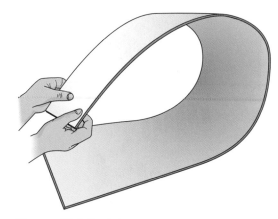

**Figure 18.1** Flexiply

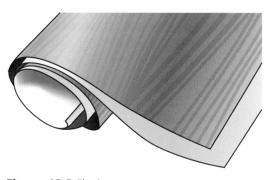

**Figure 18.2** Flexi-veneer

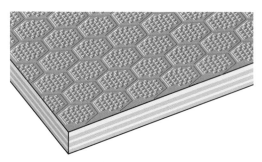

**Figure 18.3** Hexaboard

The very small particles made by nanotechnology are called nanoparticles. These usually have dimensions of less than 100 nanometres – that is, one ten-thousandth of a millimetre. The nanoparticles can be combined with other materials to make **nanocomposites** with improved properties. Although they are currently quite expensive to make, nanomaterials already have a number of applications.

## Nanomaterial coatings

Glass can be coated with a layer of nanomaterial that repels dirt and water. This can be used for windows that never need cleaning or for car windscreens that do not need windscreen wipers.

Wood can be coated with a layer of nanomaterial that repels water. This can protect it from warping and rotting.

## High-performance sports equipment

Carbon nanotubes can be added to carbon fibre to reduce the weight of the composite material CRP (carbon-fibre reinforced plastic), without reducing its strength. This is being used to make golf clubs and lightweight frames for high-performance racing bikes and tennis racquets.

## Check your understanding
Tested ☐

40 Suggest a modern material that could be used to make a curved noticeboard.

41 A company makes wooden toys for small children. Suggest how it could use nanotechnology to improve its products.

Environmental and sustainability issues

# 19 Environmental and sustainability issues

## The environment as a design consideration

When selecting the materials to be used in a product, the designer must match the performance needs of the product to the properties of the material that will be used to make it. However, the designer must also consider how the product and choice of material will affect the environment, both during the product's usable life and when it is no longer needed.

One of the first decisions is whether sustainable resources could be used to make the product. Sustainable means that with careful management we will never run out of the resource. For example, softwood from managed forests can be replaced by planting new trees. In contrast, plastics are made from oil, which is a finite resource. This means that as we use it up it is not replaced and will eventually run out.

## Life-cycle analysis (LCA)

Most products are not designed to last forever. They have a lifespan, which contains a number of different stages. This is referred to as the product life cycle.

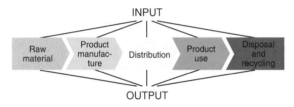

**Figure 19.1** Product life cycle

By analysing this life cycle, it is possible to see at what stages damage can be caused to the environment. This allows designers to concentrate on those stages to reduce the environmental impact. For example, a designer might need to focus on:

- reducing the amount of energy needed to make the product;
- reducing the amount of materials and packaging used;
- reducing the risk of pollution when it is disposed of at the end of its usable life.

## The six Rs

The six Rs can be used by designers as a checklist to reduce the environmental impact of a product. They stand for:

- Rethink – can what the product does be done in a different way that is less harmful to the environment?
- Reduce – can the amount of materials (and packaging) in the product be reduced?
- Refuse – this means not accepting things that are not the best option for the environment.
- Reuse – can the parts in the product be used again?
- Recycle – can the materials used to make the product be reprocessed and used again?
- Repair – can the life of the product be extended by mending it or carrying out maintenance?

Rethink and reduce are concerned with reducing the amount of resources that are required to make a product. Reuse, recycling and repair all reduce the amount of new resources that will be needed to make replacement products.

**Figure 19.2** Metal for recycling

## Design for disassembly

Most products are made from a number of different components or materials. To allow the product to be repaired, or different types of materials to be separated for reuse or recycling, products should be designed to allow them to be taken apart. One advantage to the manufacturer is that if a product is designed for disassembly, it is also often easier to assemble it in the first place.

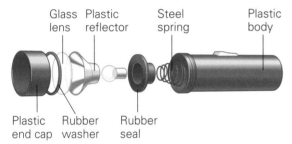

**Figure 19.3** A disassembled torch

> **examiner tip**
>
> When considering how to reduce the environmental impact of a product, use the six Rs to give you ideas.

## Check your understanding

**42** A company is designing a chair for use in school classrooms. For each of the six Rs, give an example of how that R may affect their design thinking.

**43** Explain how design for disassembly can reduce the environmental impact of a product.

# 20 Pre-manufactured components

**Pre-manufactured components** ————————————————————————— Revised ▢

Pre-manufactured components are sometimes called **standard parts**, because they are available in a range of standard sizes.

**Nails** ————————————————————————————————————————— Revised ▢

Nails are used to make a permanent joint. They are put in with a hammer or a nail gun. Most nails are made from low-carbon steel. Common types of nails include:

- round wire – used for general joinery work;
- oval wire – used for internal joinery, such as furniture;
- panel pins – used for pinning thin sheet material or for small-scale work;
- hardboard pins – used to attach hardboard to frames.

**Screws** ————————————————————————————————————————— Revised ▢

Screws are used to make temporary joints –the joint can be taken apart if necessary. The screw thread grips the material, making a stronger joint than nails. They are commonly made of steel or brass and can be used to join wood, metal or plastic. There are several different types of screw:

- countersunk – when screwed in, the head is level with or below the surface being joined;
- roundhead – used to fasten thin materials to wood; the area under the head spreads the pressure applied across the sheet material;

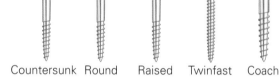

Countersunk   Round   Raised   Twinfast   Coach

**Figure 20.1** Common types of woodscrew

- raised head – used for decorative purposes, such as attaching a handle to a door;
- twinfast – used on chipboard;
- coach – a square-headed screw that is tightened with a spanner, used where great holding power is required, such as fastening metalwork vices to benches;
- self-tapping – used to join thin sheet material, such as metal or plastic.

**Nuts and bolts** ———————————————————————————————————— Revised ▢

These are used to make temporary joints. They are made from high-strength steel and most are tightened using a spanner. However, wing nuts are specially shaped to allow them to be tightened using fingers.

**Knock-down fittings** —————————————————————————————————— Revised ▢

Flat-pack furniture is designed to be supplied as parts and assembled by the user. This saves storage space at the shop and allows more units to be fitted on lorries when transporting them.

Flat-pack furniture also often uses permanent joints, such as dowels. However, most flat-pack furniture includes knock-down (KD) fittings. These allow the furniture to be assembled easily using basic tools, such as a screwdriver and a mallet.

## One-piece and two-piece corner blocks

Corner blocks are used to join together the sides of cabinets at right angles, from the inside. These are usually made from plastic.

Two-piece corner blocks are used where access for tools might be limited. One block is attached to each side of the cabinet. The two blocks are joined together using pins and a bolt, or a screw.

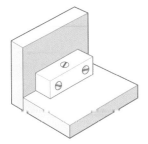

**Figure 20.2** One-piece corner block made from plastic

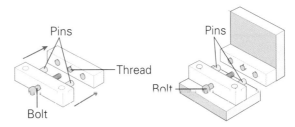

**Figure 20.3** Two-piece plastic corner block

## Scan fittings, cam locks and leg plates

Scan fittings are often used to join frames together, such as attaching the legs to a bed frame or the sides to a cabinet. An aluminium barrel is dropped into a hole drilled in one part of the frame. The barrel has a threaded hole through its centre. An Allen screw is pushed through a hole in the other part of the frame and screwed into the barrel, pulling the joint together.

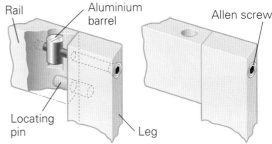

**Figure 20.4** Scan fitting

Cam locks are used to attach the front to the sides of a drawer. A threaded rod is screwed into the inside of the drawer front. The circular cam lock is dropped into a hole in the drawer side. When a screwdriver is used to turn the cam lock, this pulls the drawer front towards it, tightening the joint.

Leg plates are used to attach the legs to a piece of furniture. They use a metal plate, which is attached to two sides of the table. A rod with screw threads at each end screws into the leg. The other end passes through the plate, onto which a nut is tightened.

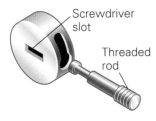
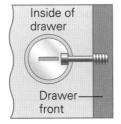

**Figure 20.5** Cam lock

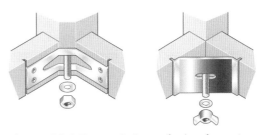

**Figure 20.6** Two variations of a leg fastening

## Check your understanding

44 Name four different types of component that could be used to join the sides of a cabinet together.

45 Explain why KD fittings are often used to make flat-pack furniture.

Fixtures and fittings

# 21 Fixtures and fittings

## Fixtures and fittings
Revised

These pre-manufactured parts help to ensure the smooth operation of doors, lids and drawers. They are often referred to as 'door furniture'.

## Hinges
Revised

Hinges are used to support parts that swing open, such as doors, windows and the tops of boxes. Fitting hinges requires a lot of care and skill, otherwise the parts will not line up.

Butt hinges are one of the most common types of hinge. They are often made from steel or brass. To improve the appearance of the joint, they are usually recessed into the edge of the wood. Back flap hinges are similar to butt hinges, but larger. They are used for large products, such as the flaps (leaves) on tables. Piano hinges are longer versions of butt hinges, used for piano lids and the boxes of snooker cues.

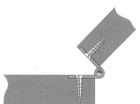

**Figure 21.1** Butt hinge

**Figure 21.2** Tee hinge

**Figure 21.3** Flush hinge

Tee hinges are used on gates and sheds. The long arm provides great support.

Flush hinges are used for small products, such as attaching the lids to small boxes. They are mounted on the surface of the wood and one flap fits inside the other when it is closed. They do not need to be recessed into the wood.

Concealed hinges are often used in kitchen cabinets. They are usually adjustable, which means that the door can easily be moved up or down, and in or out, to ensure that it is in the right place.

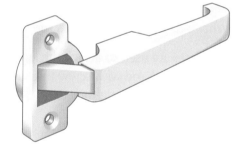

**Figure 21.4** Concealed hinge

## Catches
Revised

Catches help to ensure that doors are held shut. There are three main types:

- Ball catches are used in small cabinets and the internal doors in a house.
- Spring catches are often used in 'hidden' applications, such as inside the doors of wardrobes.
- Magnetic catches are often used in kitchen cabinets.

**Figure 21.5** Ball catch

**Figure 21.6** Spring catch

**Figure 21.7** Magnetic catch

## Locks Revised

Locks hold a door or lid closed. The difference between a lock and a catch is that a catch can be 'released' with a simple pull on the door or lid, but a lock needs an extra action to release it. There are many different types of lock:

- A hasp and staple are often used with a padlock to fasten shed doors or gates.
- Toggle catches are used to attach the top and bottom parts of a toolbox together.
- Box-style cupboard catches are used on cabinets and cupboards.

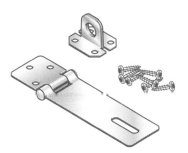

**Figure 21.8** Hasp and staple

**Figure 21.9** Toggle catch

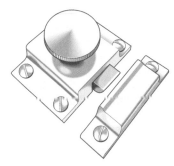

**Figure 21.10** Box-style cupboard catch

## Handles Revised

Handles or knobs allow you to open and close a door or drawer easily.

Beech     Polished brass     Anodised aluminium     Oak     Chromed finish

**Figure 21.11** A selection of drawer and cabinet handles

## Draw slides Revised

Draw slides, also known as runners, support drawers and allow them to be opened smoothly.

**Figure 21.12** Drawer runners

## Check your understanding Tested

46 Suggest a suitable hinge that could be used to attach the doors to a fitted wardrobe in a bedroom. Explain your choice.

47 Suggest a suitable component to hold the doors of a kitchen cupboard closed.

# 22 Design needs

## Design brief

The first step in the development of a new product is identifying a problem that needs to be solved. This problem is usually captured in the **design brief**. Two of the most important pieces of information in the design brief are the context and the user.

### Context

The **context** is an explanation of why there is a need for a new product. For example: *'My friends have a lot of DVDs. These are often just stored in untidy heaps and it is difficult to find the one you want to watch.'*

It is important that the context does not anticipate the solution. In the above example, that could mean saying that the final product should be a DVD rack. This would limit the creativity of the designer.

### User

Users are the people who are likely to use the product. For example, this might be teenagers, 3- to 5-year-old children, families with small children or retired people.

These users will have certain needs that they want the product to satisfy. If the **user group** is clearly defined, this can make it easier to find out what those needs are.

## Analysis of the design brief and research

The next step in the process is to analyse the design brief. This means working out what you know about the problem to be solved and what you need to find out. One way of analysing the brief is to use the five Ws method. This involves using five questions to start to explore what is needed:

- **W**ho will use the product?
- **W**here will it be used?
- **W**hy is it needed?
- **W**hat does it have to do?
- **W**hen will it be used?

There will usually be a lot of information that must be found out before the designer can be confident that the design will address the problem and meet the needs of the users. The purpose of research is to find this information. Several different types of research might be needed, to find different pieces of information:

- Product analysis involves looking at existing products and asking why they are designed in the way that they are. This might be carried out to see how they **function** and to identify their good and bad features.
- Questionnaires and interviews might be carried out to find out what the users need the product to do and the other features that they want it to have, such as its **aesthetic qualities**.
- Practical testing might be carried out, for example to identify how the product could function, its **ergonomic** requirements, and the properties of the materials that could be used.

### Function

Function means how the product will work. For example, a DVD storage system might have slots for the DVDs, with gaps between slots so that users can slide their fingers between DVDs to pull out the one they want; a moving toy might include some form of mechanism.

## Aesthetic qualities

Aesthetics means how a product appeals to the five senses. For example:

- visual appearance – what colour and shape it is;
- texture – whether the surface is rough or smooth;
- sound – what it sounds like, which is important for motors and musical instruments;
- smell and taste – for example, these can be important for children's toys or packaging.

Some aesthetic requirements are features that the user might want or like, but would not affect how well the product can fulfil its function. However, other requirements may be important needs – for example, the handle of a tennis racket needs to have texture that allows it to be gripped well.

## Ergonomics

Ergonomics is how measurements of people are used to make a product fit with a user. For example, if you were designing a motor car, you would design it to be a suitable size for adults, so that they can reach all the pedals and controls. If you were designing a pedal car for a four-year-old child, it would need to be much smaller for them to reach the controls!

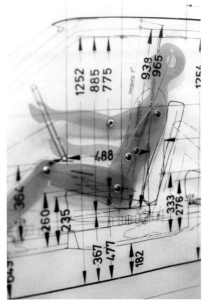

**Figure 22.1** A model used to calculate the ergonomic dimensions in a car

## Specification · Revised

The outcome of the research is usually a long list of needs that the product must satisfy. This list is called the **specification**. The designer will use it to guide their design and to evaluate how well their design solves the problem it was intended to address.

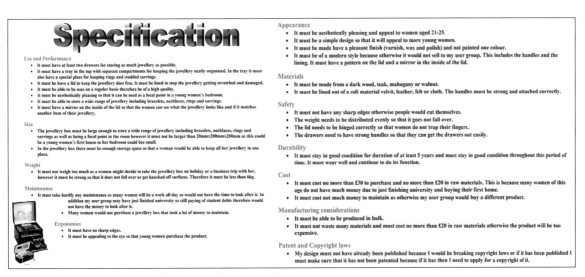

**Figure 22.2** A specification for a jewellery container

## Check your understanding · Tested

48 What information should be included in a design brief?

49 For each of the possible aesthetic qualities, give an example of a product where it is important that the product is able to do what it is needed to do.

# 23 Generating design solutions

## Generating design ideas — Revised

Once the needs that a product must meet have been identified, the next step is to generate ideas for the product. It is important to create a wide range of different and innovative ideas: this helps to give more choice for the final design, which may incorporate the best features from several different ideas.

## Sketching — Revised

A sketch is a quickly produced drawing showing some details of a product or idea. Sketching is a good way of capturing many design ideas quickly. The most promising ideas can then be developed further into a final design.

Freehand sketches can be drawn in either two dimensions (2D) or three dimensions (3D). 2D sketches show what the product looks like from one direction, typically the front or top. They are often used to show the details of an idea, such as an individual feature. 3D sketches are more difficult to draw, but give a more realistic impression of how the final product will look.

## Crating — Revised

Crating is a method of using guidelines to help draw a sketch by hand. The sketch is started by lightly drawing a cuboid just big enough to contain the shape being drawn – this is the crate. The shape is then drawn inside the crate, using it as guidelines to ensure that it is in proportion.

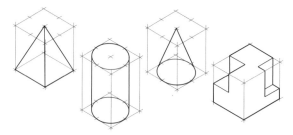

**Figure 23.1** Using a crate to sketch a shape

## Adding colour and shade to sketches — Revised

Colour or shade can be added to make a sketch look more realistic. This is called **rendering**.

### Rendering

**Rendering** means adding colour or shade to make a sketch look more realistic.

### Shading

When shading an object, it is important to consider the direction that the light is coming from. This allows you to work out which surfaces have light falling directly on to them and which surfaces will appear darker.

One way to shade a drawing is to lightly colour the whole image first. The surfaces that do not receive direct light can then be shaded again, to make them slightly darker. Finally, the surfaces on the opposite side to the light source can be shaded a third time, to make them darker again.

## Textures

Adding a texture to a shaded sketch helps to indicate the material a product is made from. Wood grain can be added using a darker pencil. Metals can be represented by showing highlights – small areas with no colour at all where light falls on them directly.

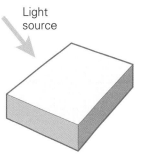

Light source

**Figure 23.2** A shaded rectangular block

**Figure 23.3** Wood grain added with a darker pencil

**Figure 23.4** Metal is represented by showing the highlights

## Annotation Revised

**Annotation** means adding notes to sketches or pictures. This is important to provide a clear explanation of a design idea. The notes might cover:

- how the product could be made;
- the sizes of the components;
- different materials that could be used;
- how features of the product work;
- how features of the design relate to the identified needs;
- how the components fit together;
- details of the finish to be used on a component.

**examiner tip**

If you are asked to sketch an idea, make sure that you use notes to clearly show the examiner that you understand the key features of the product

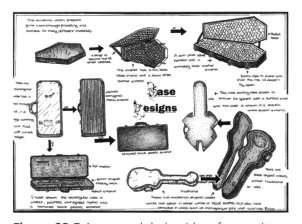

**Figure 23.5** Annotated design ideas for a guitar case

## Check your understanding Tested

**50** Produce a rendered sketch of a table for use in a classroom. Use notes to explain how it could be made.

**51** Using notes and sketches, generate an idea for a kettle.

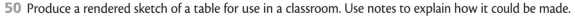

Modelling techniques

# 24 Modelling techniques

## Modelling

Making a **model** of a design idea can be used to:

- develop ideas;
- see what the final product might look like;
- identify potential problems that might occur when making the final product;
- test the features of design ideas.

Models can be seen as making 'practice versions' of a design. They are usually made from different materials from the final product. Although they do not usually have all the same properties, they are usually quicker to make and cheaper than the finished product, and can allow design features to be explored.

2D models are used to investigate details, such as how a mechanism might work. 3D models can be used to work out practical details, such as how the different parts of a product will fit together.

## Modelling using sheet materials

Corrugated card is commonly used to model 2D mechanisms or the appearance of products. It is available in a range of colours and thicknesses. It is easily cut using scissors or a craft knife, and can be joined using masking tape or sticky tape. Many designers will use recycled boxes, which are both cheaper and an environmentally friendly option.

**Figure 24.1** Corrugated card model

If a more robust model is needed, this could be made from plasticard, plastic corrugated card called corriflute, foam board or medium-density fibreboard (MDF). Depending on the material, these may be cut with a craft knife or scroll saw, and can be joined together using PVA glue or sticky tape.

## Foam modelling

High-density polystyrene, also known as styrofoam, is used to make solid 3D models. It is available in sheets or blocks up to 100 mm thickness. It can be cut easily using hand tools, such as a coping saw, or some power tools, such as a scroll saw. The surface can be smoothed using abrasive paper. Although it is only available in a limited range of colours, it can be coloured using acrylic or emulsion paints.

When using styrofoam, the shape of the item being modelled can be built up from smaller individual blocks. These can be glued together, rather than cutting a large single block, which would result in more waste.

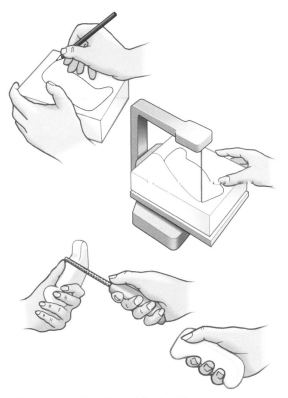

**Figure 24.2** Shaping a block of foam

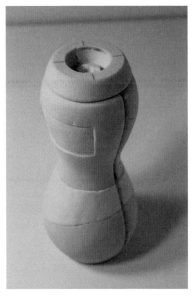

**Figure 24.3** Example of a styrofoam model

## Virtual models
Revised

**CAD** stands for computer-aided design. There are a number of CAD software packages that can be used to create virtual 3D models of a design. These can be used to model whether the parts of a product will fit together, or even to produce photo-realistic images of what the final product may look like. Virtual models can be changed very easily, adding or subtracting virtual material to the design.

## Material selection
Revised

Although they are very useful to test design ideas, models do not usually use the same materials as the final product. When choosing which materials to use in the final product, as well as the results of the modelling, the designer must consider:

- the functional requirements – what properties are needed from the materials that will be used to make the final product;

- availability – what types, shapes and sizes of material are available;

- manufacturing method – not all materials can be used with all processes; the designer must consider which processes are available;

- economics – the cost of the material and the processes used to turn it into a finished product;

- appearance and finish – what the materials will look like.

> **examiner tip**
> You should be able to explain the reasons for making a model and how models are different from the final product.

For more information on selecting materials, see Topics 11, 12, 13 and 14: Properties of materials, Wood and manufactured board, Metals, and Thermoplastics and thermosets on pages 26–33.

## Check your understanding
Tested

52 List five different materials that are used for modelling.
53 What are the benefits of modelling a product before making it?

# 25 Evaluation of design ideas

## Evaluating ideas
Revised ☐

Once a range of design ideas has been produced, these should be evaluated against the specification. This is the list of needs that the product must meet. The purpose of this may be to select ideas for further development or to select the idea that best meets the specification, so that it can be turned into the design for the final product.

If modelling has been carried out, the relevant features of the model can be tested against individual needs. Otherwise, the judgement for some needs could be based on the features of similar products, or on knowledge about materials and manufacturing processes.

Consideration might also be given to how creative the ideas are and their potential impact on the environment, such as whether they use sustainable materials.

## User testing
Revised ☐

The design ideas could also be evaluated by asking members of the user group for their opinions. As well as the needs in the specification, they could be asked questions such as the following:

● Which design will be the easiest to use? Why?

● What do you think about the style of the different ideas?

● Are there any features on any of the designs that you particularly like or dislike?

● Would you buy the product? If yes, what would you pay for it?

● How do you think the ideas compare to existing products?

At this stage it sometimes becomes apparent from the comments that the specification may not be addressing all the needs of the user group. Therefore it can sometimes be necessary to revise the specification, further develop the ideas to combine the features that the users like, and repeat the evaluation.

## Analysing a design for manufacture
Revised ☐

Some design ideas can be complex and need to be reviewed to make sure that they can be manufactured. Consideration might be given to:

● the manufacturing processes that will be needed – whether these are available and whether there are any alternatives that are more environmentally friendly (e.g. use less energy or create less waste);

● whether the design can be manufactured using computer-controlled machines;

● the materials that could be used;

● whether the number of parts can be reduced, to simplify the construction;

● the method used to attach any parts together, especially where different materials are used;

● the quantity of the product that needs to be made, and whether the design allows for easy replication of parts;

● the design of any **jigs** or templates needed.

## Selecting a design
Revised

Designers will usually record the reasons for the choice that they have made and why they have rejected the other ideas. If the specification changes at a later stage, this means that they can refer back easily, as an idea that did not meet the previous needs may satisfy the revised specification.

## Working drawings
Revised

Once the final design has been selected, a working drawing is required so that the product can be made. A working drawing, also called an engineering drawing, shows a number of 2D views of the product. These show all the relevant dimensions of the product and enough information to allow someone who has not seen the product before to be able to manufacture it.

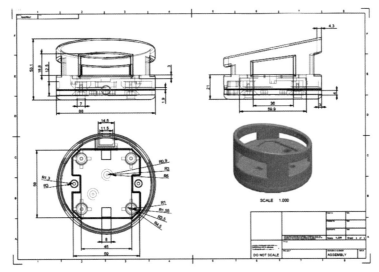

**Figure 25.1** Working drawing

## Check your understanding
Tested

54 What is the advantage of modelling before evaluating design ideas?

55 What is the purpose of a working drawing?

# 26 Rapid prototyping

## Rapid prototyping
Revised

A **prototype** is a one-off model of a final design, made to confirm that the product will meet the identified design needs and to identify any manufacturing problems. Using traditional manufacturing processes, it can take several weeks to produce a prototype, using a wide range of different equipment.

**Rapid prototyping** uses new technologies to produce a finished product in just a few days. Using a 3D drawing created with computer-aided design (CAD) software, a single computer-controlled machine manufactures the complete finished item in one operation. Depending on the complexity and size of the product, the manufacturing operation might take from a few hours to a few days.

The computer-controlled rapid prototyping machines can be very expensive – the most accurate machines can cost £100,000 or more. Although this means that rapid prototypes are expensive to make, they can greatly reduce the time between coming up with an idea and bringing a finished product to market.

For more information on CAD and computer-controlled machines, see Topic 38: Applications of computers on pages 80–1.

## How rapid prototyping works
Revised

Traditional machining processes, such as lathes, mills and drills, remove material where it is not needed. Rapid prototyping is an additive process – this means it works by adding material where it is needed in a design. The use of additive processes during the regular production of parts is referred to as **rapid manufacturing**.

The 3D design is first divided by the software into thin horizontal layers. Depending on the process and equipment used, the layers may be as thin as 0.02 mm. These layers are then sent in sequence to the rapid prototyping system, where the solid model is built up layer by layer.

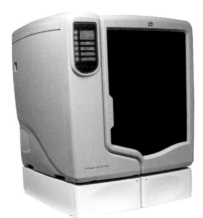

**Figure 26.1** A rapid prototyping machine

## Types of rapid prototyping system
Revised

### Laminated object manufacturing

One of the earliest systems used a vinyl cutter to cut individual layers out of adhesive-backed card or paper. The layers are then stuck together and can be painted to provide a finished prototype.

## 3D printing

This works in a similar way to an inkjet printer, with a moving head that deposits layer upon layer of material.

In one version of this process, plastic is deposited to build up the product, with the 'print head' moving up after each layer. In another version, the print head deposits an adhesive resin in the shape of the layer onto a thin layer of flour. The platform is then lowered and another thin layer of flour is deposited on top of it. The process is then repeated until all the layers have been deposited. The excess flour around the model must be carefully removed after the process.

## Stereolithography

This is one of the most widely used systems in industry. It is used to make products from plastic resin.

A stereolithography machine has a tank of liquid resin, containing a platform on which the prototype is built and a computer-controlled laser. The laser traces out the shape of a layer on the surface of the resin. This cures the resin to the shape required. The platform is then lowered by the thickness of a layer and the next layer is drawn on. The process is repeated until all the layers have been completed.

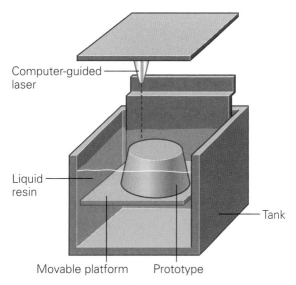

**Figure 26.2** Stereolithography

## Laser sintering

This resembles a combination of 3D printing onto powder and stereolithography. The raw material is a fine powder, which may be plastic, metal, ceramic or even a combination of these. The powder is fused together where the laser contacts it. The platform is then lowered, another thin layer of powder is deposited on top of it and the process is repeated until all the layers have been deposited.

### Check your understanding
Tested

56 How is rapid manufacturing different from traditional machining processes, such as lathes and mills?

57 Describe how stereolithography can be used to make a prototype product from a 3D drawing.

LINK TO TEXTBOOK pages 18–19, 22–6

# 27 Production planning

## Writing a production plan

Revised

A production plan lists all the activities to be carried out to make a product, in the correct sequence. One benefit of a production plan is that if a product has to be made again in the future, it will be the same.

A good production plan should include:

- the activities to be carried out, in the correct sequence;
- the materials or components to be used;
- the processes, tools or equipment to be used;
- health and safety guidance;
- time schedules for each activity.

The activities to be carried out should include both machining activities and any **quality control** activities, such as measurements needed to make sure that the product is correct. This should also include any size information needed. All of these data can be presented effectively in a table format.

| Stage | Materials used | Tools used | Safety precautions | Predicted time to complete |
|---|---|---|---|---|
| Mark wood | 12mm MDF; 9mm MDF | Pencil, ruler, set square | | 10 minutes |
| Cut wood | 12mm MDF; 9mm MDF | Circular saw | Goggles, lab coat, nothing hanging out of coat | 20 minutes |
| Sand wood | 12mm MDF; 9mm MDF | Glass paper | Goggles, lab coat, keep fingers away from glass paper | 10 minutes |
| Cut edges of wood to an angle of 60° | 12mm MDF; 9mm MDF | Circular saw | Let teacher use, goggles, lab coat | 20 minutes |
| Drill holes in sides | 9mm MDF | Screwdriver, drill bit (2.5mm) | Goggles, lab coat, keep tie in coat | 30 minutes |
| Countersink holes | 9mm MDF | Drill, countersink | Goggles, lab coat, keep tie in coat | 20 minutes |
| Attach sides to base | 12mm MDF; 9mm MDF | Screwdriver, screws, wood glue | Goggles, lab coat | 20 minutes |
| Attach top shelf to sides | 12mm MDF; 9mm MDF | Screwdriver, screws, wood glue | Goggles, lab coat | 20 minutes |
| Sand wood | 12mm MDF; 9mm MDF | Glass paper | Lab coat | 10 minutes |

**Table 27.1 A** production planning table

## Choosing and preparing materials

Revised

The designer will have selected the materials for the product based on their properties. However, there are further decisions about materials to make when planning production.

Materials are available in lots of different forms – for example, metals can be strips, sheet or bars. Each of these forms will be available in different sizes. Where possible, the manufacturer will usually use a form and size of material that is close to the size of the finished product. This reduces the cost of machining and means that there is less waste, so is also usually better for the environment.

At the same time, the manufacturer will also have to consider which processes he has available to convert the materials into the final product. Some materials are not suitable for certain processes, such as vacuum forming. For reasons of cost and sustainability, the manufacturer will usually prefer to use the process that has the lowest energy and labour-time requirements. Process choices may also be limited by moral and cultural issues. For example, the local community may place value on handmade items rather than using machines, in order to provide jobs.

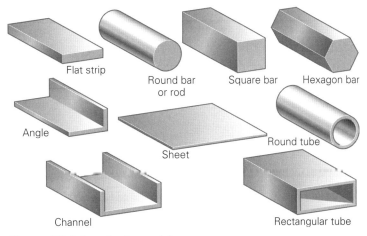

**Figure 27.1** Standard metal forms

For more information on selecting materials, see Topics 11, 12, 13 and 14: Properties of materials, Wood and manufactured board, Metals, and Thermoplastics and thermosets on pages 26–33.

## Overcoming production problems                                    Revised ☐

Problems can arise during production that could affect the planned activities. For example, machines may break down or not be available. To address this, it is usually recommended to identify in the plan alternative machines or processes that could be used.

Where problems arise at individual operations in the plan, flow charts can be an effective tool to manage them. They are commonly used to control the operation of machines or to respond to quality control problems, where parts have been machined to the wrong size.

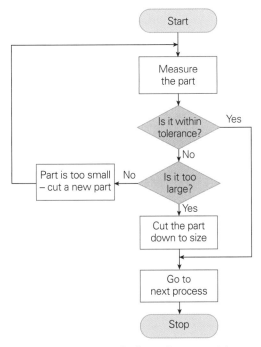

**Figure 27.2** A simple flow chart used for quality control during machining

## Check your understanding                                          Tested ☐

58 What things should be included in a production plan?

59 Explain the things a manufacturer must consider when choosing which form of material to use to make a product.

Product evaluation

# 28 Product evaluation

## Product evaluation
Revised ☐

Existing products might be evaluated to identify their good features and areas for improvement, so that these can be used when designing a product. A 'new' product that has just been designed will be tested to determine its **fitness for purpose**. This means how well it satisfies the needs that it was designed to meet.

## Existing products
Revised ☐

The first step in evaluating an existing product is to establish its function. This means determining what it was designed to do. It is then important to identify who the intended user or market is. This allows a better understanding to be developed of the needs that the product was supposed to meet.

When examining the product, the materials it is made from should be identified. The reasons that these materials were used should be explained. Usually, this will be a result of one or more of the properties of the material. This will further help to identify the needs that the designer was trying to meet.

When evaluating existing products, it is usual for a variety of different products, all designed to meet the same need, to be examined. These products may be made from different materials. Examining several products can make it easier to identify the needs and to compare different features.

## New products
Revised ☐

When evaluating new products, the starting point is usually the specification. This is the list of needs that the product must meet.

## Testing products
Revised ☐

Once the needs that a product must meet have been identified, it can be tested against each of them.

The tests to be carried out will depend on the needs, and the properties of the design and the materials that address those needs. For example, if the specification says that:

● the product should weigh less than 2 kg, it could be weighed on scales;
● the product should be a certain shade of blue, it could be compared against a colour chart;
● the product should be able to support at least 5 kg, it could be loaded with 5 kg to see if it fails.

For more information on material properties, see Topic 11: Properties of materials on pages 26–7.

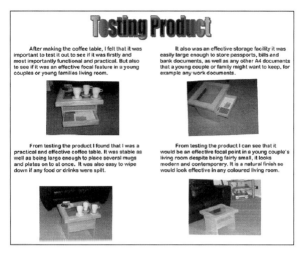

**Figure 28.1** A small coffee table being tested

## User testing

This means testing by the intended user in the intended location. Ideally, it should be tested in conditions that represent the full range of what it will experience during its life. This will include when it is stored and transported, as well as when it is used.

User testing is often used to gather the opinions of users about the product. These might be obtained using interviews or questionnaires.

## Identifying improvements

Revised

During testing, if any of the needs are not met, improvements to the product should be identified that would allow them to be achieved. Even if a need is being satisfied, it can still be worth considering whether it could be met in other ways. For example, could there be a cheaper or more environmentally friendly way of meeting that need?

The sort of improvements that are often identified include:

- changes to design features, such as increasing the thickness of a section to make it stronger, or making innovative changes to the design to reduce cost;
- using different materials, such as using an alternative with better properties or replacing a non-renewable material with a sustainable one;
- modifying the way the product is manufactured, such as using an additional process to remove sharp edges, or an alternative process to reduce energy needs or waste.

**Figure 28.2** Some details of how a product could be improved

## Check your understanding

Tested

**60** What is meant by 'fitness for purpose'?

**61** Give three examples of the type of improvements that could be identified in a product following testing.

*Preparing and measuring materials*

# 29 Preparing and measuring materials

## Preparing and measuring materials
Revised

To make an accurate product in a school workshop, the materials need to be prepared, and the shapes needed must be measured and marked out. The parts made should also be checked to make sure they are correct.

## Measurement and testing
Revised

Measurements are usually taken from a **datum** face. This is the side, edge or end of the material from which the dimensions are measured. Without a flat surface to work from, it is likely that the measurements will be inaccurate.

Most measurements have a **tolerance**. This is the amount that they can vary from the stated value and still be acceptable.

Most measurement tools can be used with either wood, metal or plastic. The choice of which measurement tool to use will depend on the accuracy of measurement needed.

### Rules

A rule is a long piece of material, with measurements marked along the edge. It is usually made from steel or plastic. The rules used in school workshops are usually accurate to about 0.5 mm.

### Vernier callipers

These use a sliding section over a steel bar. They are used to measure thickness or diameter, to an accuracy of around 0.02 mm.

**Figure 29.1** Steel rule

### Micrometer

A micrometer tightens on to a piece of material. It is usually the most accurate piece of equipment used in a school workshop, with a typical accuracy of 0.01 mm.

## Marking out
Revised

There is a wide range of tools that are used to help in **marking out** the lines to be cut or processed on a piece of material. Each type of tool is used either to carry out a different task or for a different material.

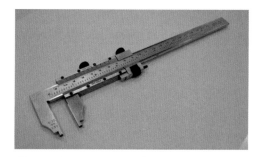

**Figure 29.2** Vernier callipers

### Scriber

Scribers are usually made from very hard tool steel. They are used like a pencil, to mark out lines on metal or plastic. They do this by leaving a 'scratched' mark in the material. In comparison, the pencil marks used to mark out wood can usually be rubbed away using an eraser.

### Dividers

Dividers are similar to a compass, but with two hard points. They are used to mark circles and curves on metals and plastic, by 'scratching' a line.

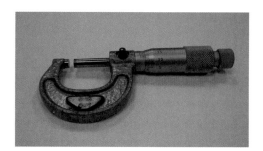

**Figure 29.3** Micrometer

## Punches

Punches are used on metal. A centre punch is used to mark the centre of a hole to be drilled. A dot punch is used to highlight lines to be cut and to mark the centres of circles that will be cut out. Punches are usually made from very hard tool steel.

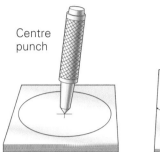
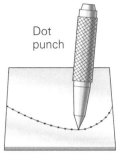

**Figure 29.4** Centre and dot punches

**Figure 29.5** Dividers

## Try square

A try square usually has a wooden stock and a carbon steel blade. It is used on wood and plastic, to mark a line at 90 degrees to an edge.

Engineers' squares have a metal stock and blade. They are used for the same purpose with metals.

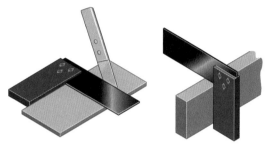

**Figure 29.6** Try square

## Templates

A template is a shape that can be placed onto a material, then drawn or cut around. They are often made from paper or card. The main advantage of a template is that it allows a complicated shape (such as a guitar body) to be marked out quickly. When making lots of products, it also helps to ensure that each product is the same shape.

**examiner tip**

It is important to know which tools are used to mark out the different types of material.

## Check your understanding

Tested ☐

62 A piece of metal needs to have a hole marked for drilling. The hole must be positioned at right angles to two datum points. Which tools should be used to mark this out?

63 A manufacturer makes 100 skateboards per day, in groups of ten. Give two reasons why a template might be used to mark them out.

Wasting processes using hand tools

# 30 Wasting processes using hand tools

## Wasting
Revised

**Wasting** means removing the material that is not needed in a product, usually by cutting it away.

## Sawing
Revised

Saws are the most common tools used to cut material. In general, the harder the material to be cut, the smaller the teeth on the saw. Using the wrong type of saw can damage the saw and the material, and may result in safety problems.

| Type of saw | Used with | Used to |
| --- | --- | --- |
| Hand saw | Wood | Make straight cuts in large pieces of wood |
| Tenon saw | Wood | Make straight cuts |
| Coping saw | Wood, plastic | Cut curves in thin material |
| Hacksaw | Metal, plastic | Make straight cuts |
| Junior hacksaw | Metal, plastic | Make straight cuts in small-scale work |
| Piercing saw | Metal, plastic | Pierce holes and cut shapes in fine work |

**Table 30.1** Types of saw

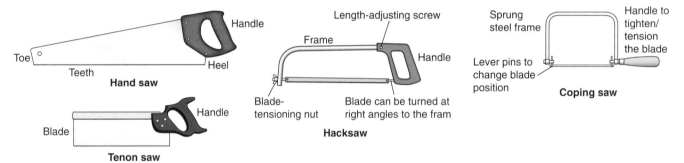

**Figure 30.1** Types of saw

## Drilling
Revised

Drilling is used to make holes in material. The task that can be carried out depends on the type of drill or bit used:

● Twist drills are used to make small-diameter holes in wood, metal or plastic.

● Flat bits and Forstner bits are used to make holes in wood up to 50 mm diameter.

● Hole saws are used to make holes up to 75 mm diameter in wood.

● Centre bits are used to bore shallow holes in wood.

The drills and bits can be held in either a brace or a portable drill, or in machine tools, such as pillar drills or a centre lathe.

## Chiselling
Revised

Chisels are used to cut and shape wood. They are exceptionally sharp and both hands should be kept behind the cutting edge at all times. There are three main types:

● Firmer chisels are used for general-purpose work.

● Bevel-edge chisels are used in corners – for example, when cutting a dovetail joint.

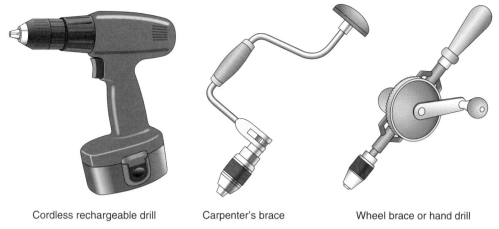

Cordless rechargeable drill          Carpenter's brace          Wheel brace or hand drill

**Figure 30.2** Types of drill

- Mortice chisels are thicker than the other two, and can be hit with a mallet. They can be used to level out waste wood without breaking.

There are also cold chisels, which are a special type of chisel used to remove metal. These must be hit with a hammer.

## Files and rasps — Revised

Files have rows of small teeth that work like very small chisels. They are used to shape and smooth metal and plastic. They are available in a variety of lengths and shapes, to make different profiles in a product.

Rasps are similar to files, but have coarser teeth. They are used to shape and smooth wood.

## Planing — Revised

Planes are used to shape and smooth wood. The cutting action of a plane is similar to that of a chisel, held in a frame at a specific angle.

The two most common types of plane are jack planes, which are used for the quick removal of wood, and smoothing planes, which are used for fine finishing and planing end grain. These look similar, but jack planes are slightly longer – 350 mm, compared to 250 mm for a smoothing plane. Special types of plane are available to cut out rebates, grooves, curved surfaces and to level the shoulders of joints.

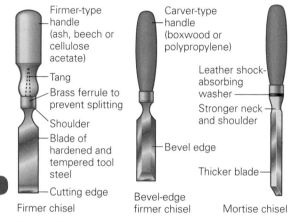

Firmer-type handle (ash, beech or cellulose acetate)

Tang

Brass ferrule to prevent splitting

Shoulder

Blade of hardened and tempered tool steel

Cutting edge

Firmer chisel

Carver-type handle (boxwood or polypropylene)

Leather shock-absorbing washer

Stronger neck and shoulder

Bevel edge

Bevel-edge firmer chisel

Thicker blade

Mortise chisel

**Figure 30.3** Types of chisel

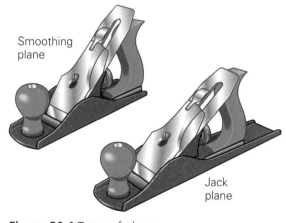

Smoothing plane

Jack plane

**Figure 30.4** Types of plane

## Check your understanding — Tested

64 Which tool would be used to cut a curve in a sheet of plastic?

65 An artist has designed a sculpture to be made by hand from a block of wood. It includes sections that are long and flat, and other areas with intricate shapes. List the wasting tools that the artist might use, explaining what each is used for.

# 31 Wasting processes using machine tools

## Using machine tools — Revised

Machine tools include powered devices such as lathes, milling machines, sanders and pillar drills. They reduce the physical effort required to carry out a process. They also carry out the process much faster than would be possible by hand.

Before using a machine tool, you should always check that the machine is safe to use. For example, all guards should be in place and electrical leads should not be loose, damaged or frayed. You should also check the settings on the machine, such as the tool speed and movement. If there is an error, this could cause damage to both the machine and the workpiece, as well as safety issues.

## Sawing — Revised

Machine saws are very versatile. Scroll saws are used to cut thin sheets of wood or plastic – in effect they are like automated coping saws. Jigsaws are used to cut sheet material. They have variable speeds and a range of different blades for wood, plastic or metal.

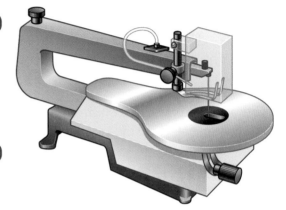

**Figure 31.1** Types of machine saw

## Turning — Revised

**Turning** is the process of making a round component using a lathe. Wood lathes are used to turn wood and centre lathes are used to turn metal or plastic. Lathes work by holding a piece of material in a chuck attached to the headstock spindle. The workpiece is rotated at high speed, while a cutting tool is pushed against it, until the desired cylindrical or tapered shape is achieved.

Lathes can also be used to produce flat faces on the end of cylindrical components, drill holes and cut screw threads.

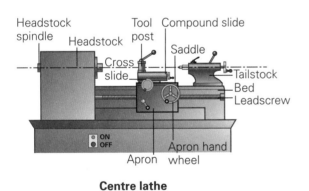

**Centre lathe**

**Wood lathe**

**Figure 31.2** Types of lathe

## Milling — Revised

**Milling** machines are used to machine large surfaces of a material to make them flat. They are also used to cut slots and grooves in metal, plastic and wood.

Milling involves securely attaching the material to a work table on the machine, known as the bed. The bed can be moved in three directions (side to side – X axis, front to back – Y axis, and up and down – Z axis), using rotating levers. A high-speed rotating tool is then lowered against the material, and the machine bed is moved so that the tool can contact all parts of the area to be machined. When metal is being machined, coolant is often used to reduce the heat generated and to reduce wear.

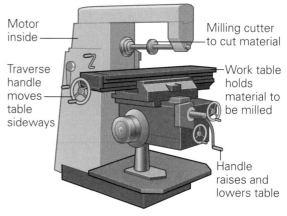

Horizontal milling machine

## Routing Revised

Routers are like smaller versions of milling machines, in that they use a tool that rotates at high speed. They are used to cut slots, grooves and to make fancy-shaped edges in wood.

The workpiece to be routed must be held securely. On a manually operated router, the casing has handles so that it can be moved by hand. However, if the tool is moved too fast, this can cause a poor quality of cut. If the tool is moved too slowly, the friction can cause the cut surface to char. Many routers used in school workshops are controlled by computers, rather than moved by hand.

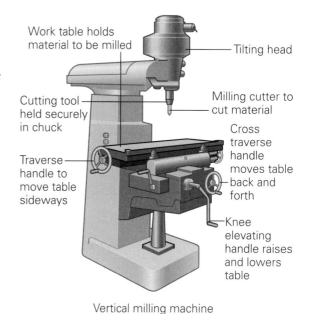

Vertical milling machine

**Figure 31.3** Milling machines

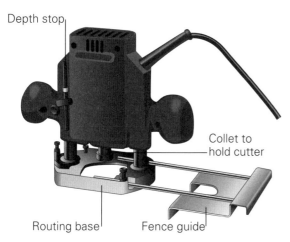

**Figure 31.4** Router

## Check your understanding Tested

66 State two safety checks that should be carried out before using a machine tool.

67 Describe two different machine tool processes that could be used to make a flat face on the end of a metal cylinder.

# 32 Deforming: bending processes

Deforming: bending processes

## Deforming
Revised ☐

Deforming processes change the shape of a material while it is in the solid state.

## Bending wood
Revised ☐

Wood will only bend by a very small amount before it breaks. This makes **forming** difficult. If a curved shape is needed, this is often cut from a solid piece of wood. However, this makes lots of waste.

### Kerfing

One method of bending wood is to use a saw to cut a series of evenly spaced, thin slots in it, which allow it to be bent. This is called **kerfing**. It is only suitable if the inside of the curved piece will not be visible in the product.

### Steam bending

**Steam bending** involves placing the wood in a sealed chest full of steam. A piece of wood 25 mm thick typically needs about an hour in the steam chest. The wood absorbs the hot moisture and becomes more pliable. It is then bent in a **former**. Once it cools, it will retain its new shape.

### Laminating

**Laminating** is one of the most commonly used processes to bend wood. It involves gluing thin strips of wood, called veneers, together. These are clamped in a shaped former until the glue sets. From the side, the shaped product looks similar to plywood, as the different layers can be seen.

## Bending metal
Revised ☐

Simple bends can be produced in thin pieces of metal by applying force. For example, a metal strip can be held in a vice and hammered, or it could be bent around a former. Larger metal sheets can be bent accurately using rollers or bending jigs.

Thicker pieces of metal can be softened using heat before the force is applied, usually by hammering or squeezing. This is known as **forging**.

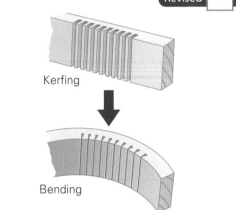

Kerfing

Bending

**Figure 32.1** Kerfing

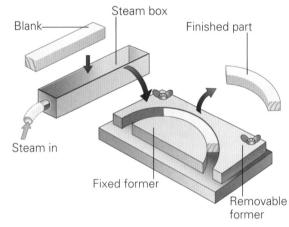

Blank

Steam box

Finished part

Steam in

Fixed former

Removable former

**Figure 32.2** Steam-bending former

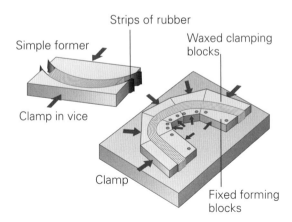

Strips of rubber

Simple former

Waxed clamping blocks

Clamp in vice

Clamp

Fixed forming blocks

**Figure 32.3** Forming a laminated wooden shape

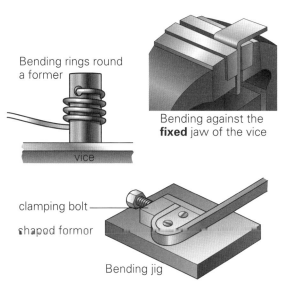

Bending rings round a former

vice

Bending against the **fixed** jaw of the vice

clamping bolt

shaped formor

Bending jig

**Figure 32.4** Examples of metal bending

**Figure 32.5** A simple machine to fold sheet steel

## Line-bending plastic

Revised

Line bending is used to produce simple bends in sheets of thermoplastic, such as acrylic. It is carried out using a strip heater.

The material is heated along the line where the bend is to be made. Care must be taken not to put the plastic too close to the heating element, otherwise it may blister, melt or burn. When it is soft enough to be flexible, it can be removed and bent into shape. A former or bending jig is often used if an accurate bend is needed. It must be held in position until it cools, so that it retains the bend.

**Figure 32.6** Electric strip heater

> **examiner tip**
>
> If you are asked to sketch and describe a process, make sure that you annotate your sketches. The notes help to explain clearly what your sketch shows and demonstrate to the examiner that you understand the process.

## Check your understanding

Tested

**68** Describe how laminating would be used to make the seat of a wooden chair.

**69** List three deforming processes that involve heating material so that it can be bent. Identify the material that each of these processes is used with.

# 33 Deforming: moulding processes

Deforming: moulding processes

## Press moulding
Revised

**Press moulding** is used with sheets of thermoplastic, such as acrylic or high-impact polystyrene (HIPS). It produces simple, hollow, 3D shapes like bowls and trays.

It involves using a former made of two parts:

● The plug produces the shape required. It should have angled sides and smooth rounded corners, so that the finished moulding can easily be removed from it.
● The yoke presses the soft plastic over the plug. The hole in the yoke needs to be slightly bigger than the plug, to allow for the thickness of the plastic.

Most two-part formers include guide pegs, to make sure that the plug and yoke line up correctly.

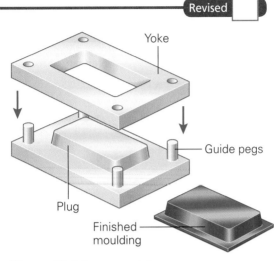

**Figure 33.1** Press moulding

The plastic sheet to be moulded is heated in an oven until it is flexible. It is then positioned onto the plug, usually using heat-resistant gloves. Next it is pushed down with the yoke. The two parts of the former are usually clamped together until the plastic has cooled down. After it is removed from the former, any excess plastic is cut away from the finished moulding.

## Blow moulding
Revised

**Blow moulding** is commonly used to make plastic bottles. A tube of softened plastic called a parison is put inside a **mould**, which is usually made from two parts. Air is then injected inside the plastic tube, which inflates like a balloon to fill the shape of the mould. Once the plastic has cooled in its new shape, the mould is opened and the product is removed.

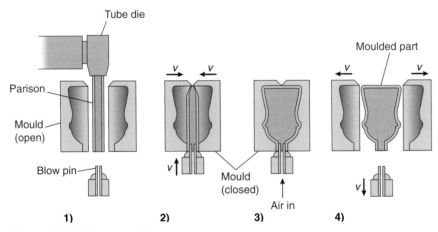

**Figure 33.2** Blow moulding

## Vacuum forming

**Vacuum forming** is used to shape sheets of thermoplastic, such as HIPS or polypropylene. It is used to make simple 3D shapes, such as yoghurt pots.

The plastic sheet is clamped between a heater and a mould. When it is softened, the mould is raised up and the air in the cavity is pumped out. The air pressure of the atmosphere forces the soft plastic against the mould. After the plastic has cooled, it is taken off the mould and any excess material is cut away from the required shape.

The design of the mould is critical. It must be heat-resistant and have a smooth surface, as any defects might show on the formed product. Its sides must be tapered to give a draft angle, so that the plastic can be removed once it has cooled. Any corners must be rounded off, to avoid the risk of the plastic splitting as it is formed. If there are recesses in the mould, it may need to include vent holes to allow the air to be pumped out. The moulds used in school workshops are often made from MDF.

**Figure 33.3** Vacuum-forming process

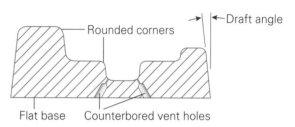

**Figure 33.4** Vacuum-forming mould

> **examiner tip**
>
> You should be able to describe the sequence of steps involved in each of these forming processes.

## Check your understanding

70  With the use of sketches, describe the blow-moulding process.

71  Explain four important requirements for a vacuum-forming mould.

# 34 Reforming processes

## Reforming
Revised

Reforming creates a shape through processes that involve a change of state of the material used, such as allowing a liquid to set or cool to make a solid.

## Die casting
Revised

Metal casting involves pouring melted material into a mould of the required shape and allowing it to cool. It can be used to make complicated 3D shapes.

In **die casting**, the moulds (dies) are typically made from steel. They are very expensive to make, but can be used many times to make lots of products. The metals cast using the process must have a low melting point, such as aluminium, pewter or zinc, which is used to make camera bodies and car door handles.

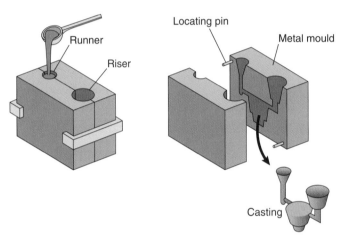

**Figure 34.1** Die casting

Die casting can also be used with some plastics. Thermoplastics can be heated until they melt. Alternatively, some plastic resins can be cold-poured (without heating). They set due to a chemical reaction within the material.

## Injection moulding
Revised

**Injection moulding** is used for the large-scale production of thermoplastic parts. The process is similar to die casting in that it involves melting the material and uses an expensive metal **die**. However, the plastic is squirted into the mould under pressure. It is used to make complicated 3D products, ranging from the screw caps on plastic bottles to car dashboards, the casings used for electronic products and garden furniture.

The raw material used is granules or pellets of the thermoplastic, which are fed into a hopper on the injection-moulding machine. A rotating feed screw takes the granules through a heating chamber, where they are melted. When enough liquid plastic has reached the shot chamber, the feed screw is rammed forward to inject it into the die under pressure. The die might contain spaces for one large part or many small parts. The mould is then opened to release the finished mouldings.

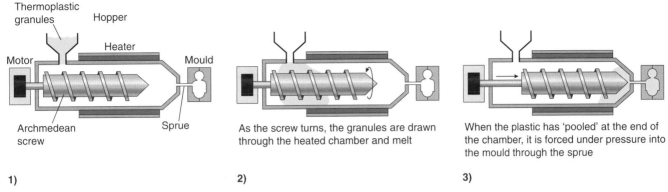

Figure 34.2 Injection moulding

Revised

## Extrusion

The **extrusion** process is used to make long, continuous lengths of uniform section, such as plastic pipes, guttering and curtain tracks. It is also used to coat metal wires with plastic and to supply the parison used in blow moulding.

For more information on blow moulding, see Topic 33: Deforming: moulding processes on pages 70–1.

> **examiner tip**
>
> You should be able to explain the differences between the injection-moulding process and the vacuum-forming process.

Extrusion involves forcing molten thermoplastic material through a die shape. The feed system is similar to an injection-moulding machine, except that the liquid material is continuously forced through the die by rotation of the feed screw and is not rammed to increase the pressure. The extruded shape cools after leaving the die and can be rolled into coils or cut into suitable lengths.

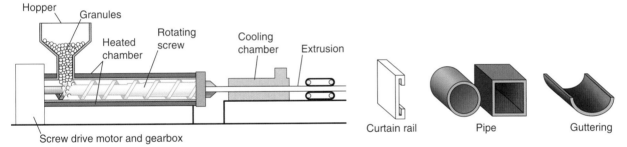

Figure 34.3 Extrusion

## Check your understanding

Tested

72 What is a die?

73 Explain the differences between extrusion and injection moulding.

# 35 Fabricating

## Fabricating
Revised

**Fabricating** means making products by joining parts together. There are two different groups of joining technique:

● temporary – the join can be taken apart if needed; temporary joining methods include screws, nuts and bolts, and knock-down joints;

● permanent – joints cannot be taken apart without damaging the material; permanent joining methods include adhesives, nails, wood joints, pop riveting, brazing, soldering and welding.

For more information on screws, nuts and bolts, knock-down joints and nails, see Topic 20: Pre-manufactured components on pages 44–5.

## Adhesives
Revised

There are lots of different types of **adhesive**. The surfaces to be joined must be thoroughly cleaned before the adhesive is applied. Many can only be used with one type of material:

● Polyvinyl acetate (PVA) is used with wood.

● Solvent cement is used with thermoplastics. It works by melting the two surfaces to be joined together.

● Epoxy resin can be used with a wide range of materials and can be used to bond different materials together, such as wood and metal. It comes in two parts (a resin and a hardener) and it must be mixed immediately before use.

● Cyanoacrylate, also known as superglue, and contact adhesive will both bond a wide range of materials.

## Wood joints
Revised

There are lots of different designs of wood joint. Most are usually glued with PVA. In general, the greater the area where the two pieces of wood touch each other, the stronger the joint and the more effort required to make it.

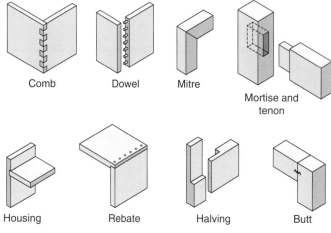

Comb    Dowel    Mitre    Mortise and tenon

Housing    Rebate    Halving    Butt

**Figure 35.1** Wood joints

## Pop rivets

Pop riveting is used to fasten thin sheet metal and other materials. Holes are drilled in the pieces to be joined, through which the rivet is inserted. The rivet gun is squeezed, pulling the pin through, expanding the rivet head. The pin then breaks off, leaving the formed rivet with the pin head in it.

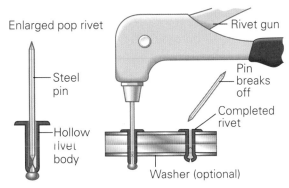

**Figure 35.2** Pop riveting

## Heat processes to join metal

**Soldering** is used to join metal parts together, such as electronic components and the copper surface of a circuit board. It involves melting a metal alloy with a lower melting point than the metals being joined. The melted material flows into the joint between the parts, forming a physical bond. It is important that the joint is cleaned thoroughly. Flux, a chemical mixture, is used to keep the surfaces free from oxidation when the heat is applied.

**Brazing** is similar to soldering, but is carried out at much higher temperatures. A brazed joint is usually much stronger than a soldered joint.

The strongest method of joining two pieces of metal is **welding**. It involves melting the edges of the parts to be joined. The heat source used might be an electric arc, a laser or the flame from an oxyacetylene torch. A filler metal might be added to fill any gaps between the two parts.

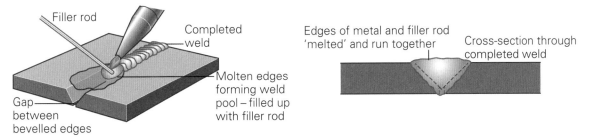

**Figure 35.3** Welding

## Check your understanding

74 A manufacturer needs to join a thin sheet of plastic to a thin sheet of metal. Which joining techniques could be used?

75 What is the difference between soldering and welding?

Health and safety

# 36 Health and safety

## Responsibilities of the designer
Revised

Designers must make sure that products can be made safely and are safe to use:

- They must ensure that the products are fit for purpose and will remain safe in normal use and during maintenance.
- Products must conform to the safety standards in the countries where they are sold. For example, in the UK, toys display the lion mark to show that they have met the legal requirements.
- Where necessary, products should include instructions on use.
- Possible dangers should be labelled. For example, a light bulb may be marked with its safe maximum wattage.

## Risk assessment
Revised

**Risk assessment** is the process of identifying hazards in the working environment and actions necessary to reduce or eliminate the potential for harm. It is a legal requirement and involves the following steps:

- For each activity being carried out, identify the potential hazards.
- Evaluate the likelihood of the hazard occurring and the potential risk of harm.
- Identify the control measures needed to prevent the risk of injury.

## COSHH
Revised

When chemicals are used in products or during manufacturing, they have the potential to cause harm. For example, workers could have an allergic reaction to a paint that they are using.

**COSHH** stands for the Control of Substances Hazardous to Health and is a legal requirement. It can form part of a risk assessment. It requires employers to assess the risk from using substances and chemicals. Most substances should have COSHH data sheets available from their manufacturers.

## Personal safety
Revised

Employers must provide safety equipment to eliminate or reduce the hazards identified by the risk assessment. Two common pieces of safety equipment are machine guards and fume extractors. Machine guards protect against:

- debris flying off a machine, either from the workpiece or from a tool that breaks;
- moving parts that could cause the user to become entangled in a machine;
- sharp cutting tools.

Dust and fume extraction is used to protect against breathing in dust – for example, from a sanding machine – or toxic fumes – for example, from paint or plastic resin.

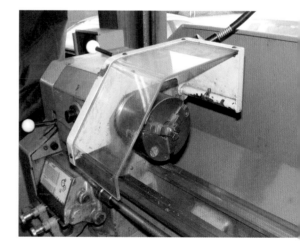

**Figure 36.1** Lathe guards

It is also important to prevent additional hazards arising by disposing of waste quickly and appropriately. Not doing so could cause risks ranging from trips and falls to fire hazards, or it could pollute the environment.

## Personal protective equipment Revised

If it is not possible to eliminate or reduce a risk in another way, a risk assessment might state that personal protective equipment (**PPE**) must be worn. PPE is special items that you wear to protect yourself against an identified risk.

| Item of PPE | Purpose | Example of machines/processes when it is necessary to wear the item of PPE |
|---|---|---|
| Safety goggles | Protects eyes | Pillar drill, lathe, belt sander |
| Face mask | Protects against breathing in dust and fumes | Paint spraying, disc sander |
| Visor | Protects eyes and face | Casting, welding |
| Apron | Protects clothes and skin | Casting, pillar drill, lathe, painting |
| Leather gloves | Protects hands and arms | Vacuum forming, casting |
| Disposable gloves | Protects hands and skin | Using chemical adhesives, painting |

**Table 36.1** Personal protective equipment

## Accident procedures Revised

Every workplace should have an accident procedure. This helps to limit the effect of any accident that happens, by making sure that everyone knows what to do.

## Safety symbols Revised

It is important to comply with safety signs.

- Blue signs are mandatory – you must do what they say.
- Red circles tell you something you must not do – for example, No entry.
- Black and yellow triangle signs are warnings.
- Green rectangles give you information – for example, to show the location of emergency exits.
- Orange squares or diamonds are warnings of hazards – for example, flammable substances.

**examiner tip**

Examiners often ask you to state the safety precautions that should be used with a process.

Wash your hands

Wear eye protection

Wear ear protection

Corrosive

Toxic

Chemicals

**Figure 36.2** Safety signs

## Check your understanding Tested

76 What is risk assessment?

77 What PPE should you wear when spray-painting a wooden product?

# **37** Industrial production

Industrial production

## Scale of production
Revised ☐

The scale of production refers to the number of parts to be made. This has a major effect on the choice of production method that is used to make them.

## One-off production
Revised ☐

One-off production refers to making one or a very small number of products. The type of products range from spectacle lenses and designer jewellery to satellites and special parts needed to repair large machines.

It is often carried out using machines that are very flexible in how they are used. This means they can be used to make lots of different types of products. They are often manually controlled by an operator, as this can be more cost-effective than spending time programming a computer to control them.

In industry, many prototypes are produced as one-off products. These allow a product to be evaluated before it is made in larger quantities. New technologies such as rapid prototyping or rapid manufacturing can be used to make complicated prototypes in a single computer-controlled operation. This can greatly reduce the amount of time it takes to develop new products.

For more information see Topic 25: Rapid prototyping on pages 54–5.

## Batch production
Revised ☐

If a manufacturing company was making 100 chairs, it would not make them one at a time. It would make 100 seats, 100 backs and 400 legs, and then assemble them.

**Batch production** involves making a set quantity of the same product. The size of the **batch** might range from less than ten to a few thousand, depending on the product. The batch might be repeated at a later date if it is needed again. Products made this way include parts for Formula 1 cars, musical instruments and most household furniture.

Batch production is often carried out using computer-controlled machines. These can usually carry out machining operations faster than manual machines. Templates and jigs are often used to mark up and position the parts. They can be quite expensive, but with batch production the cost is divided between all the parts in the batch.

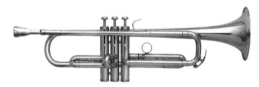

**Figure 37.1** Example of a batch-produced product – a trumpet

For more information on computer-controlled machines, see Topic 38: Applications of computers on pages 80–1.

## High-volume production

Revised

High-volume production is where large quantities of one type of product are made. The quantities involved might range from a few hundred to tens of thousands of products per day, depending on the type of product. The products are often identical. Many of the items that we use every day are produced in high volumes. This includes nuts and bolts, mobile phones, cars and bars of chocolate.

This is sometimes called mass production and is carried out on a production line. Due to the large quantity of products being made, high-volume production is often carried out on dedicated machines. This means that each machine is used only to make one product. The machines will probably use **fixtures** to position the parts. These are similar to jigs, but are permanently attached to the bed of the machine.

The machines will usually be computer-controlled. Many may also have automation or robot arms to load and unload the parts into them, which speeds up the process and reduces the labour costs.

## Globalisation

Revised

Companies can choose to make their products in every country where they sell them. However, improved transport and communication systems give them the opportunity of globalisation. They can set up a factory in one country and transport the finished products all round the world. This allows them to take advantages of different working conditions and wage costs in different countries.

One disadvantage of globalisation is the environmental impact of transporting goods all round the world. An advantage is that products can be cheaper for the user or make more profit for the manufacturer.

For more information on globalisation, see Topic 5: Refuse on pages 14–15.

**Figure 37.2** Container ship

## Check your understanding

Tested

78 What is meant by 'batch production'?

79 List the three main production methods. For each, give an example of a product made using that method.

Applications of computers

# 38 Applications of computers

## CAD

CAD stands for computer-aided design. This means any use of computer software to support the design process. The most common use of CAD in schools is to produce drawings and 3D images.

Most CAD drawing software allows you to create and manipulate an image on screen. This might be a 2D or a 3D image, depending on the software. You can create a drawing of your own design idea, for example, then zoom in on features or move the image round, so you can look at it from different angles. The image created using 3D CAD drawing packages is often used to model how parts will fit together or to give a realistic impression of what the final product will look like.

In business, CAD has almost completely replaced drawing by hand for working drawings. This is because CAD drawings are very accurate and can be easily changed, without having to start again from scratch.

## CAM

**CAM** stands for computer-aided manufacture. This means using a computer to control the machine that is used to make a product. The CAM software on the computer looks at either the CAD drawing or an entered program, and converts this into a string of numbers that will control the movement and speed of the machine. This is known as computer numerical control (**CNC**). All machines that are controlled by CAM are CNC. These range from lathes, milling machines, routers, machining centres and laser cutters, to sticker cutters and rapid prototyping units.

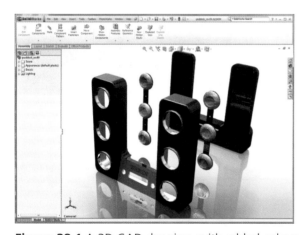

**Figure 38.1** A 3D CAD drawing, with added colour to show what the finished product could look like

**Figure 38.2** CNC milling machine

## Applications of CAD/CAM

Revised

CAD/CAM is widely used in industry for making products in quantity. Compared to machines controlled by operators, CAM machines:

- can operate at faster machining speeds;
- produce products that are the same size every time – better consistency and repeatability.

Time is needed to produce a CAD drawing and to program a CAM machine. Due to this, when making one-off products it is sometimes more cost-effective to use manually controlled machines than CAD/CAM. However, CAD/CAM is able to produce complicated machined shapes that human operators cannot make. It can also be used to operate rapid prototyping machines to quickly make complicated models and prototypes.

For more information on making one-off products, see Topic 25: Rapid prototyping on pages 54–5.

## Types of software

Revised

Several other types of software are commonly used in business:

- Text software, such as word processors like Microsoft® Word, are used for writing reports, sales brochures and letters to customers.
- **Databases** such as Microsoft Access® are used to store and process information, such as the names and addresses of customers.
- Spreadsheets such as Microsoft Excel® are used to process information. They can manipulate tables of information, to work out the costs of products or to record the amount of products sold, and create graphs showing the results.
- Graphics software ranges from CAD drawing software to packages such as Adobe® Photoshop®, which is used to edit photographs.

## Storing and sharing data

Revised

CD-ROMs, DVDs, external hard drives and network servers can all be used to store data and electronic files. Memory sticks, also called pen drives, can be used to store data and also to transfer data between different computers. It is also easy to transfer data using the internet, either through a broadband connection or using Wi-Fi, a system of high-frequency radio signals.

**examiner tip**

Examiners often ask you to explain the advantages of CAD and CAM. Do not just write 'faster' or 'accurate'. Write sentences that describe a benefit and how CAD or CAM allow it to be achieved.

## Check your understanding

Tested

80 What do CAD, CAM and CNC stand for?

81 List two advantages of using CAD/CAM to make products in large quantities.

## 39 Systems and control

### Managing quality

Most companies operate systems to ensure that the products they make are good quality. These systems usually have two parts:

● **quality assurance** – this means making sure that a product will be made correctly;

● **quality control** – this means measuring parts after they have been made to check that they are correct.

When making a batch of products, devices like jigs, fixtures, templates and patterns are an important part of quality assurance.

For more information on batch manufacture, see Topic 37: Industrial production on pages 78–9.

### Jigs

Jigs are devices that hold and position a workpiece. They help to make sure that the workpiece is held safely and that machining operations are always carried out in the same place. When using jigs, it is not usually necessary to mark out the feature that the jig is designed to machine.

For example, two holes have to be drilled in 100 pieces of wood. If the wood is to fit onto a product, it is vital that the distance between the holes is consistent and accurate. A jig would be designed that would hold the workpiece in position each time, and guide the drill bit so that every hole is in the correct place.

The disadvantage of jigs is that they can be time-consuming to make. It is often only cost-effective to make a jig if there is a large batch of products to make.

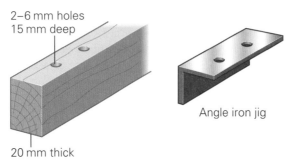

2–6 mm holes
15 mm deep

20 mm thick

Angle iron jig

**Figure 39.1** A manufacturing jig for drilling two holes in a piece of wood

Some common features of jigs are:

● They hold the workpiece securely in place, using grooves, side pieces or clamps.

● They have end or side stops. If a datum end of the workpiece is pushed against the stop, this means that the area to be machined should be in the correct position relative to the tool.

● They may include slots or holes to guide the tool to the correct place.

### Fixtures

A fixture is a type of jig that is attached to the tool or base of a machine.

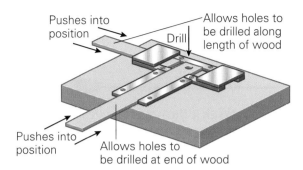

Pushes into position

Drill

Allows holes to be drilled along length of wood

Pushes into position

Allows holes to be drilled at end of wood

**Figure 39.2** Drilling jig

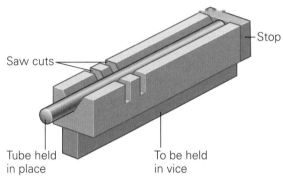

Saw cuts

Stop

Tube held in place

To be held in vice

**Figure 39.4** Sawing jig

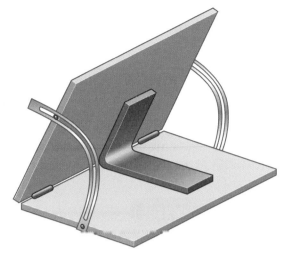

**Figure 39.3** Bending jig

## Templates
Revised

**Templates** are shapes that can be drawn, scribed or cut around to mark out a piece of material. They can also be used to check that a finished item is the correct shape. If a batch of parts are to be made, it is often quicker to make a template for a complicated shape than to mark out the parts separately. Templates can also help to ensure accuracy and consistency, as all the parts will be marked out identically.

The template can be made from any thin, rigid material. Thick card may be suitable if only a small number of parts are being made. Manufactured board or sheet plastic might be used if the template will be required again in the future. These are less likely to suffer from wear or be damaged.

## Patterns
Revised

Like templates, **patterns** are shapes that can be used for marking out. They are often made from paper or thin card, which is glued onto the surface of the material. They tend to be used when the shape is very complicated or ornate.

> **examiner tip**
>
> Examiners sometimes ask you to design a jig for a simple application. If you know the general principles of jigs, you can apply these to almost any application.

## Check your understanding
Tested

82  What is meant by a 'manufacturing jig'?
83  A manufacturer has to make three guitars for a customer. What would be the advantages of using a template for the body?

# 40 Quality

## Quality of design and quality of manufacture
Revised

Quality of design means how well a design should be able to carry out the tasks that the product is needed to do. Quality of manufacture is how well a product is made. These are not the same thing. Even if you have a brilliant design, if the product is badly made it might not work. If the product is badly designed, even if it is well made it may not be able to do all the things that it is needed to do.

## Materials and processes
Revised

The quality of a finished product is affected by the materials and processes chosen to make it. While ensuring that the product must be adequate for what it is needed to do, the designer must usually balance the level of quality needed with the cost of the product.

A wooden garden bench, for example, could be made from teak or pine. Teak could provide a hard and attractive product – however, it is expensive. Pine would be much cheaper, but it is softer, making it more susceptible to damage, and less weather-resistant. So long as the pine bench is strong enough, the designer may choose to use this material on cost grounds.

Two of the methods used to attach the parts of a bicycle frame are brazing or welding. Brazing costs less, but welding makes a stronger joint. If a manufacturer was making a mountain bike for rugged, off-road cycling, they would probably use welding. However, for a road bike they may use a brazed joint, as it could be strong enough and cheaper to make.

For more information on soldering, brazing and welding, see Topic 35: Fabricating on pages 74–5.

## Dimensional accuracy
Revised

The dimensions of products might be based on the strength or other properties required, or to ensure that parts fit together.

When parts are being machined, there can be small differences in their finished sizes. These can result, for example, from the temperature of the workpiece increasing, wear of the tools, variations between different batches of raw materials or vibration of the machine. For this reason, the dimensions shown on working drawings are usually given a tolerance. This is the amount that a measurement can vary from its nominal value and still be acceptable.

For example, if the length of a part must be 20.0 mm +/−0.5 mm, the product would be acceptable if the dimension was between 19.5 and 20.5 mm. 19.6 mm would be acceptable, but 20.6 mm would not.

The tolerance must take into account how the part will be used – for example, if two parts need to fit together, they must still be able to do so even if they are at the opposite extremes of the tolerance.

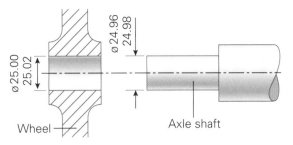

**Figure 40.1** Dimensions of a hole-and-axle shaft showing the range of possible sizes

Quality control means checking a part after it has been made, to make sure that it is the correct size. There are lots of different types of checks that can be carried out:

● Measurements can be made using rulers, Vernier callipers and micrometers. They can also be checked using Go–No Go gauges. The item being checked should fit the 'Go' part of the gauge, but not the 'No Go' part.

● Visual checks can be carried out for the colour, surface finish and overall appearance of the product.

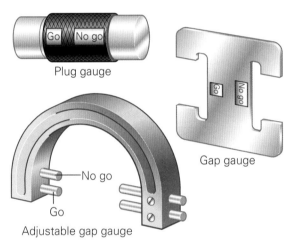

**Figure 40.2** Types of gauge

> **examiner tip**
>
> When you are asked to describe a quality control check, describe at what stage of manufacture it would be carried out and how it would be carried out.

For more information on measurement tools, see Topic 29: Preparing and measuring materials on pages 62–3.

## Check your understanding · Tested

**84** Explain how quality of design is different from quality of manufacture.

**85** Why is it necessary to have a tolerance on a working drawing?

# Answers to Check your understanding questions

1 Sustainable resources are resources that will not run out, such as sunlight and wind energy; renewable resources, such as wood from managed forests, are replenished naturally within a short period of time.

2 The company could reduce the amount of the materials it uses or use materials with a smaller carbon footprint; it could use energy from sustainable sources during manufacture or reduce energy requirements from non-sustainable sources; it could increase the number of goods it transports on each lorry it sends. It could also use carbon offsetting.

3 Rethink involves looking at the need that a product is addressing and asking if that need can be met in a more environmentally friendly way.

4 More than one film could be put on a DVD or it could be replaced with a download; the packaging could be replaced with a cardboard sleeve.

5 Built-in obsolescence means designing a product so that it only lasts for a certain period of time.

6 Conceive, design, make, use, disposal.

7 Finite means that there is only a certain amount of a resource on our planet and it will eventually run out if we continue to use it.

8 E.g. wind, tidal, geothermal, hydroelectric, solar.

9 Wind power generates electricity by turning propellers, which turn a turbine. Solar power creates electricity directly when sunlight falls on to a solar panel.

10 E.g. plastic made from oil, as this is a non-renewable resource.

11 E.g. Advantages: lower costs to the user or more profits for the company. Disadvantages: environmental pollution due to increased transportation; working conditions and environmental regulations in the country of manufacture may be below the standards that we would be prepared to accept.

12 Reuse means using the parts of a product to make another product.

13 E.g. Using old jam jars to store pencils; using an old tyre to make a swing; making sandals from old tyres.

14 Secondary recycling means reprocessing the material and using it to make a different type of product.

15 Steel can be removed from domestic waste using magnets. You have to look at the recycling symbols on other materials.

16 E.g. access panel or door, held together using screws.

17 E.g. electrical circuits – may contain charge; plug – may not be as strong and robust after repair.

18 E.g. television remote control – narrow enough to make it easy to grip, buttons large enough to be easy to push, but separated enough so that fingers can push only one at a time.

19 Market pull – changes in fashion, such as user preferences for a different colour; technology push – developments in technology, such as the miniaturization of electronic components; environmental pressures – e.g. the need to reduce pollution.

20 Inclusive design means designing products so that they can be used by those who have physical disabilities, not just the 'average' user.

21 The aim of the Ethical Trading Initiative (ETI) is to ensure that a suitable standard of working conditions is achieved for all workers.

22 A bicycle tyre – e.g. flexibility, ductility, hardness; the wing of an airliner – e.g. strength-to-weight ratio, strength, malleability; a disposable cup from a drinks machine – e.g. strength, chemical resistance, thermal conductivity, flexibility, malleability; the body of an electric kettle – e.g. thermal conductivity, electrical conductivity, toughness.

23 Compressive strength – this will show how much the metal will resist the change in shape; ductility – this will show how much the shape of the metal can be changed without breaking; malleability – this will show how easy the metal is to form into the wire.

24 Medium-density fibreboard.

25 (a) Teak or any suitable hardwood, by name; Parana pine or any suitable hardwood, by name; blockboard or any suitable manufactured board. (b) E.g. cost – manufactured board would be the cheapest option, followed by softwood. Hardwood would be the most expensive option.

Aesthetics (appearance) – oak- or veneer-covered blockboard may be the most attractive option.

Sustainability – manufactured boards use more of the tree, so may be the most environmentally friendly option; hardwoods grow slowly, so may be the least environmentally friendly option.

Size – manufactured boards are available in greater sizes, whereas timber planks may need to be joined together to make the table into the size needed.

26 A metal that does not contain iron.

27 Steel contains both iron and carbon. As it is a mixture of these two elements, it is an alloy.

28 Ferrous metals – e.g. cast iron, mild steel, stainless steel; pure non-ferrous metals – e.g. aluminium, copper, lead, zinc; non-ferrous metal alloys – e.g. duralumin, brass, bronze.

29 E.g. aluminium or copper, as both are good conductors of heat and have good corrosion resistance.

30 The shape of a thermoplastic can be changed by heating it until it softens, then cooling it in a new shape. The shape of a thermosetting plastic cannot be changed by heat once it has been formed.

31 E.g. melamine formaldehyde – this is a thermoset, so it will not change shape when heated. It is also stain-resistant, scratch-resistant and odourless.

32 Hardening and annealing both involve heating steel to a high temperature. However, in hardening, the steel is cooled quickly by quenching. In annealing, it is allowed to cool slowly.

33 The toughness of work-hardened mild steel can be increased by normalising. It involves heating the steel above its upper critical point, then allowing it to cool in still air.

34 A material made by combining two or more different materials, which remain physically distinct within its structure.

35 E.g. fibreglass boat hulls, CRP bodies in high-performance sports cars, CRP frames for racing bikes, Kevlar™ body armour.

36 The surface of a metal product is first cleaned to remove any oil or grease. The part to be coated is put in a tank containing a chemical solution and an electrical contact. An electrical current is passed through the part and a thin layer of metal slowly builds up on it.

37 E.g. sealer and polyurethane varnish or yacht varnish, as these add shine and provide good protection against moisture. Oil and wax would provide some protection, but would not be as effective. Paint would not be a preferred choice, as it would hide the natural appearance of the wood.

38 A material that has a property that reacts to changes in its environment. This change is reversible when the environment changes again. It can also be repeated many times.

39 E.g. shape memory alloy – fire alarm switches; thermochromic strip – thermometers; photochromic glass – sunglass lenses that become darker when exposed to light; quantum tunnelling composite – contact sensors.

40 Flexiply.

41 A water-resistant coating could be used to stop the wood being damaged or rotting, or to reduce the need for cleaning.

42 E.g. Rethink – could an alternative form of seating be used – e.g. benches or ledges that can be attached to a wall?

Reduce – could it be made smaller and still do the same job? Could three legs be used instead of four?

Repair – could the product be designed so that broken legs or seats can be replaced, rather than throwing the whole chair away?

Reuse – could they reuse the legs from existing chairs in schools?

Recycle – could recycled plastic be used to make the seat?

Refuse – customers may choose not to buy it if it is not environmentally friendly.

43 Design for disassembly can allow the product to be repaired, or different types of materials to be separated for reuse or recycling. These reduce the need for new materials to make replacement products.

44 Nails, screws, one-piece corner blocks, two-piece corner blocks, scan fittings, dowels.

45 Knock-down fittings allow the furniture to be assembled easily using basic tools, such as a screwdriver and mallet; also cheeper storage and transportation.

46 E.g. back-flap hinge – because it is suitable for large items and stronger than a butt hinge; concealed hinge – for appearance, as it cannot be seen from outside; tee hinge – as it is strong, but only if a 'rustic' appearance is acceptable.

47 E.g. spring catch or magnetic catch.

48 The brief should state the context and identify the user group.

49 E.g. visual appearance – the colour of a warning light; texture – the grip on a tennis racket; sound – the chime of a bell; smell – a toilet should be odourless and resistant to picking up bad smells; taste – food packaging should not change the taste of the food.

50 The response should be a rendered sketch of a table, including notes explaining how it could be made.

51 E.g.

52 E.g. card, plasticard, foam board, corriflute, MDF and styrofoam.

53 It is cheaper and quicker to make a model than a final product. Models allows you to test if the design features of the product work or to get an impression of what it looks like.

54 If modelling has been carried out, the relevant features of the model can be tested against individual needs rather than basing the evaluation on other products or opinions.

55 A working drawing shows all the relevant dimensions of the product and enough information to allow a third party or machine to manufacture it.

56 Traditional machining processes remove material where it is not required. Rapid manufacturing is additive – it adds material where it is required.

**57** The 3D design is first divided by the software into thin horizontal layers. These layers are then sent in sequence to the stereolithography machine. A laser traces out the shape of a layer on the surface of a resin bath. This cures the resin to the shape required. The platform is then lowered by the thickness of a layer and the next layer is drawn on. The process is repeated until all of the layers have been completed.

**58** A production plan should include: the activities to be carried out, in the correct sequence; the materials or components to be used; the processes, tools or equipment to be used; health and safety notes; time schedules for each activity.

**59** The manufacturer will usually use a form and size of material that is close to the size of the finished product. This reduces the cost of machining and means that there is less waste, so is also usually better for the environment. The manufacturer must also choose a form that is suitable for use with the machines that are available for use.

**60** Fitness for purpose means how well a product meets the needs that it was designed to meet.

**61** E.g. changes to design features, such as increasing the thickness of a section to make it stronger; using different materials, such as replacing a non-renewable material with a sustainable one; using alternative manufacturing processes, to reduce energy needs or waste.

**62** An engineer's square to identify the position of the hole, and a centre punch to mark it.

**63** Marking out would be much quicker and every board would be the same.

**64** Coping saw.

**65** For the flat sections, a jack plane to remove material, followed by a smoothing plane. For the shaped sections, a mortice chisel to remove material, with either a firmer chisel or a bevel-edge chisel for detail work. Possibly a rasp.

**66** All guards should be in place and electrical leads should not be loose, damaged or frayed.

**67** Turning – the cylinder is held in a chuck and rotated at high speed, while a cutting tool is pushed against it, to make a flat face.

Milling – the cylinder is fixed standing on the bed of a milling machine. A high-speed rotating tool is then lowered against the material and the machine bed is moved until all of the face has been machined flat.

**68** A former would be made for the seat. Thin strips of wood, called veneers, would be glued together. These are clamped into the former until the glue sets.

**69** Steam bending – wood; forging – metal; line bending – plastic.

**70** Suitable sketches should be accompanied by a description similar to the following: (1) A tube of softened plastic is put inside the mould. (2) Air is injected inside the plastic tube, which inflates like a balloon to fill the shape of the mould. (3) Once the plastic has cooled, the mould is opened and the product is removed.

**71** E.g. It must be heat-resistant, so that the hot plastic does not damage it. It must have a smooth surface, so no defects show on the formed product. It must have sides tapered at a draft angle, so that the product can be removed once it has cooled. Any corners must be rounded off, so that the plastic does not split as it is formed. If there are recesses in the mould, it may need to include vent holes to allow the air to be pumped out.

**72** A metal mould that can be used many times.

**73** In extrusion, the feed system continually forces the liquid material through the die by rotation of the feed screw, whereas in injection moulding the liquid material is rammed through each time enough builds up. The product made by extrusion is continuous, but the product made by injection moulding is a single item (or group of items).

**74** Adhesives (epoxy resin) or pop riveting.

**75** In soldering, the joint between the parts is formed by a filler metal. The parts being joined are not melted. Welding is carried out at much higher temperature and involves melting the edges of the parts to be joined.

**76** Risk assessment is the process of identifying potentially dangerous situations in the working environment and the actions necessary to reduce or eliminate the potential for harm.

**77** Face mask, apron, disposable gloves.

**78** Batch production means making a set number of identical products, before changing production to the next product.

**79** One-off production – e.g. spectacle lenses; batch production – e.g. parts for Formula 1 cars; high-volume production – e.g. nuts and bolts.

**80** Computer-aided design, computer-aided manufacture and computer numerical control.

**81** E.g. CAM machines are usually more accurate than human workers; they can also operate at faster machining speeds; the parts will all be the same.

**82** A jig is a device to hold or position a workpiece.

**83** Reduced time to mark out the bodies; all the guitars will be the same shape (consistency).

**84** Quality of design refers to how well a design should be able to carry out the tasks that the product is needed to do. Quality of manufacture refers to how well the actual product is made.

**85** A tolerance is necessary as products can vary from the nominal dimensions. It shows what amount of variation would be acceptable without affecting the performance or fit of the product.

# Glossary

Adhesive – a chemical used to attach or glue together two pieces of material.

Aesthetic qualities – how an object appeals to the five senses.

Alloy – metals that are a mixture of two or more elements or pure metals, such as brass or stainless steel.

Annealing – heating metal to soften it, make it less brittle and easier to work.

Annotation – adding notes to sketches or pictures.

Anthropometrics – the study of body sizes and properties.

Batch – a set number of identical products.

Batch production – making a set number of identical products, before changing production to the next product.

Biodegradable – a material that breaks down and rots away in the ground.

Blow moulding – using air pressure to blow softened plastic into shape inside a mould.

Brazing – a metal-joining technique where a filler metal is used to form a physical bond between the parts being joined.

Built-in obsolescence – designing a product so that it lasts for only a certain period of time.

CAD – computer-aided design, the use of computer software to support the design process.

CAM – computer-aided manufacturing, the use of computers to control machines.

Carbon footprint – a measure of how much greenhouse gases are produced by something.

Carbon offsetting – carrying out projects to reduce carbon emissions, to balance out the production of greenhouse gases.

Carburising – adding carbon to the surface of a piece of steel, to increase its hardness.

Case hardening – hardening the outer skin of mild steel.

Chemical resistance – the ability of a material to resist being damaged by chemicals.

CNC – computer numerical control, the control of a machine by computers using strings of numbers.

Composite material – a material made by combining two or more different materials, which remain physically distinct within its structure.

Context – the situation or problem that has given rise to the need for a solution.

COSHH – Control of Substances Hazardous to Health, a way of identifying the risks associated with specific substances.

Database – a document for storing and processing information.

Datum – a standard position or flat surface that measurements are taken from.

Deforming – changing the shape of a material while it is in the solid state.

Design brief – a short statement of the problem to be solved.

Die – a mould made from metal that can usually be reused many times.

Die casting – a reforming process that involves pouring liquid material into a metal mould of the required shape.

Disassembly – taking a product apart.

Ductility – how much a material can be stretched without breaking.

Eco-design – considering the whole life of a product when it is being designed, from design to disposal, including its use of materials and energy.

Eco-footprint – a measurement of the effect of a product or person on the environment.

Elasticity – the ability of a material to be deformed and still return to its original shape.

Electrical conductivity – how easily electricity can pass through a material.

Electroplating – depositing a layer of metal using electrolysis.

Ergonomic – using measurement data to ensure that a product is the correct 'fit' for a user.

Extrusion – forcing a material through a die to produce lengths of uniform section.

Fabricating – making products by joining parts together.

Ferrous metal – metal that contains iron, such as steel.

Finishing – changing the surface of a material in a useful way.

Fitness for purpose – how well a product satisfies the needs that it was designed to meet.

Fixture – a work holding and positioning device similar to a jig, but attached to the base of a machine.

Flexibility – the ability of a material to bend without permanently changing shape.

**Forging** – hammering or squeezing metal into shape, usually when it is hot.

**Form** – the size and shape of a piece of material or a product.

**Former** – a block made to hold material in the shape required.

**Forming** – changing the shape of a piece of material without wasting (cutting away) material.

**Function** – how a product does what it is needed to do.

**Globalisation** – considering the world as a market; manufacturing in one country to supply markets in several countries.

**Hardness** – the ability of a material to resist cutting and scratches.

**Hardwood** – wood obtained from deciduous trees, which lose their leaves in the autumn.

**Inclusive design** – designing products so that they can be used by people with disabilities.

**Injection moulding** – a reforming process that involves forcing molten plastic into a die.

**Jig** – a work holding and positioning device.

**Kerfing** – cutting a series of uniform slots in a piece of wood to allow it to be bent.

**Laminating** – gluing thin strips of material together.

**Landfill** – burying waste and unwanted products under the ground.

**Malleability** – the amount that the shape of a material can be permanently changed without breaking it.

**Manufactured boards** – wood-based materials that are made by compressing and bonding pulp, small pieces or thin sheets of wood with adhesive.

**Marking out** – identifying the lines or shape to be cut or processed on a material.

**Milling** – the process of using a rotating cutter to produce a flat surface, groove or slot.

**Model** – a 2D or 3D representation of a design idea, usually made from a different material to the final product.

**Mould** – a shaped block over which a material can be formed into a required shape.

**Mouldings** – shaped sections machined from timber.

**Nanocomposite** – a composite material where one or more of the materials combined in it is a nanomaterial, with dimensions of less than 100 nanometres.

**Non-ferrous metal** – metal that does not contain iron, such as aluminium, copper or zinc.

**Normalising** – heating steel and allowing it to cool naturally in still air.

**Painting** – applying liquid which dries to form a coating on the surface.

**Pattern** – a shape that can be used to mark out the forms of the parts of a product.

**Photochromic** – changes colour in response to changes in the level of light.

**Polishing** – rubbing or buffing the surface.

**Pollution** – contamination of the environment.

**PPE** – personal protective equipment, specialist items worn to reduce the risk of harm or injury.

**Press moulding** – forming a hollow shape from a softened plastic sheet.

**Product life cycle** – the stages a new product goes through, from conception and design to eventual disposal.

**Prototype** – a one-off model of a final product, made to confirm that it will meet the design needs and identify any manufacturing problems.

**Pure metal** – metal made from a single element, such as aluminium, copper or lead.

**Quality assurance** – a system to make sure that a product will be made correctly.

**Quality control** – testing or measuring a product after it has been made to see if it is correct.

**Quenching** – cooling metal quickly in oil or water.

**Rapid manufacturing** – the use of additive processes such as rapid prototyping in the production of products.

**Rapid prototyping** – making a 3D prototype in layers using computer control.

**Recycling** – reprocessing materials so that they can be used to make other products.

**Reforming** – creating a shape from material involving a change of state, such as casting liquid metal and allowing it to cool into a solid.

**Rendering** – adding colour or shade to make a sketch look more realistic.

**Renewable** – a resource that is naturally replenished or replaced within a short period of time.

**Risk assessment** – the process of identifying potentially dangerous situations in the working environment and actions necessary to reduce or eliminate the danger.

**Seasoning** – drying green timber to remove moisture.

**Smart material** – a material that changes its properties in response to changes in its environment.

**Softwood** – wood obtained from coniferous trees, which retain their leaves all year round.

Soldering – a metal-joining technique where a filler metal is used to form a physical bond between the parts being joined.

Specification – the list of needs that a product must meet.

Standard parts – pre-manufactured components available in set sizes.

Steam bending – softening the fibres of wood with steam to allow the wood to be bent.

Strength – the ability of a material to resist breaking when a force is applied to it.

Strength-to-weight ratio – a measure of the strength of a material compared to its weight.

Sustainable – able to continue indefinitely.

Tempering – heating steel to removing excess hardness and brittleness after hardening.

Template – a shape that can be used to mark out the form of a product.

Thermal conductivity – how easily heat can pass through a material.

Thermochromic – changes colour in response to temperature.

Thermoplastic – a type of plastic that will soften when heated so that its shape can be changed. It will harden into the new shape as it is cooled. This process can be repeated many times.

Thermoset – a type of plastic that can be formed into a shape once only. It cannot change its shape when heated again.

Tolerance – the amount that a measurement can vary from its nominal value and still be acceptable.

Toughness – the ability of a material to withstand knocks and blows.

Turning – the process of making a round or tapered component using a lathe.

User group – a clearly defined group of people who will be the users of a product.

Vacuum forming – making thin hollow items over a shaped mould using air pressure.

Wasting – removing the material that is not needed in a product, often by cutting, grinding or drilling.

Welding – a metal-joining process where the edges of the parts to be joined are melted.

Work hardening – an increase in the hardness of a metal due to bending or hammering.

# Index